# Contents

W0009460

# Advice for parents and carers

**Children learn best when they do not feel under pressure and when they are free to explore ideas. Be flexible. If your child is distracted or tired they will not gain much from the practice.**

This book allows children to apply what they have learned in key areas of the curriculum. The questions have been written to a higher level than usual and are meant to be challenging and to provide stretch. Supporting learning and understanding in this way will strengthen your child's grasp of key concepts. The questions can be used to assess areas to work on further. Follow up by offering opportunities to consolidate learning in a real-life setting and allow a break before working on further questions.

Please note that if your child does not do well in answering these questions it is not an indication of poor performance in the National Tests. If you have any concerns, please discuss them with your child's teacher.

This book includes 20 tests, each with a particular mathematical focus. They have been written in the same style as the National Test questions but the tests are shorter in length as they focus on one topic at a time only. You can work through them in order or you and your child can choose a topic which interests you the most or you feel needs further practice.

You may want to start by taking the test to assess your child's understanding of the topic. Use the answer grids to record their marks and identify *Workbook* links.

Review these areas and practice skills in the *Workbook*.

Alternatively, start working with the *Workbook* to review and practise a topic. Complete the corresponding test in this book to assess how well they have understood the topic.

# Advice for children

Are you ready to take the challenge? The questions in this book are tricky but they will help you to see how much you understand. Sharpen your skills in the *Workbook* first then try the questions here.

Don't worry if you don't manage to answer every question or if you get some answers wrong. We learn from our mistakes. If some questions really stump you, go back to the *Workbook* and check those skills again.

- Find a quiet place to work.

- Have a positive mindset – focus on what you know. Remember that mistakes make our brains grow!

- Take your time – don't start the challenge if you are in a rush to do something else.

- Review your work.

# Progress chart

| Test | Taken | Practised | Achieved |
|---|---|---|---|
| 1. Counting and representing number | | | |
| 2. Comparing and ordering numbers | | | |
| 3. Adding and subtracting mentally | | | |
| 4. Inverse operations | | | |
| 5. Multiplying and dividing mentally | | | |
| 6. Problem solving with multiplication and division | | | |
| 7. Fractions | | | |
| 8. Equivalent fractions | | | |
| 9. Fractions of shapes | | | |
| 10. Fractions of sets of objects | | | |
| 11. Fractions of quantities | | | |
| 12. Length | | | |
| 13. Mass and temperature | | | |
| 14. Capacity and volume | | | |
| 15. Money | | | |
| 16. Time | | | |
| 17. 3D shapes | | | |
| 18. 2D shapes | | | |
| 19. Turns | | | |
| 20. Charts and tables | | | |

**SCHOLASTIC**

# Reward Certificate

## Well done!

*I've aimed higher with SATs Challenge*

Name: _____ Date:_____

*My strongest areas are:*

_____

_____

*I will challenge myself to fly higher in:*

_____

Marks

**1.** Write the missing numbers.

0　5　10　[ ]　20　[ ]　[ ]　[ ]

1

**2.** Look at this diagram.

What **number** is represented?

[ ]

1

**Write** the number in the correct place on the number line.

90 —————————————— 100

1

**3.** Write the missing numbers.

54　52　[ ]　[ ]　46　[ ]　[ ]

1

**4.** **Draw** a picture that shows **63**.

Marks

1

Marks

**5.** Write the missing numbers.

30  60  ☐  120  ☐  ☐  ☐

2

**6.** This is part of a 100 square.

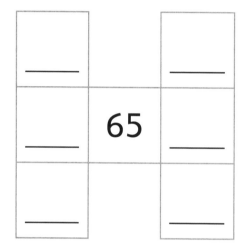

Fill in the missing numbers.

2

**End of test**

Marks

**1.** **Partition** 59 in three different ways.

 + [ ] = 59

[ ] + [ ] = 59

[ ] + [ ] = 59

1

**2.** Order from **greatest** to **least**.

68     23     79     16     83

greatest  least

[ ] [ ] [ ] [ ] [ ]

1

**3.** Look at this number.

## 58

What does the **5** represent?

1

What does the **8** represent?

1

**Marks**

4. Circle the **greatest** number.

34          87          14

1

Explain how you know it is the greatest.

_____

_____

_____

_____

_____

_____

_____

_____

1

5. Compare these numbers.

Write **>**, **<** or **=** in each box.

43 ☐ 98

30 + 4 ☐ 20 + 14

87 ☐ 37

1

**6.** Anya is thinking of a number.

It has six 10s and three 1s.

Ben is thinking of another number.

It has two 10s more and three 1s less than Anya's number.

What is Ben's number?

Marks

> Show
> your
> working

2

End of test

## 3: Adding and subtracting mentally

1. Use your **number bonds** to answer these.

   Show exactly what you do.
   One has been done for you.

   $35 + 8 = 35 + \boxed{5} + \boxed{3} = \boxed{43}$

   $58 + 7 = 58 + \boxed{\phantom{0}} + \boxed{\phantom{0}} = \boxed{\phantom{0}}$

   $76 + 5 = 76 + \boxed{\phantom{0}} + \boxed{\phantom{0}} = \boxed{\phantom{0}}$

   $64 - 5 = 64 - \boxed{\phantom{0}} - \boxed{\phantom{0}} = \boxed{\phantom{0}}$

   1

2. Use **doubling** to add these numbers.

   Show exactly what you do.
   One has been done for you.

   $34 + 35 = 34 + \boxed{34} + \boxed{1} = \boxed{69}$

   $25 + 26 = 25 + \boxed{\phantom{0}} + \boxed{\phantom{0}} = \boxed{\phantom{0}}$

   $32 + 33 = 32 + \boxed{\phantom{0}} + \boxed{\phantom{0}} = \boxed{\phantom{0}}$

   $41 + 42 = 41 + \boxed{\phantom{0}} + \boxed{\phantom{0}} = \boxed{\phantom{0}}$

   1

**SCHOLASTIC** Skills Test Papers

Marks

**3.** Use **rounding** and **adjusting** to answer these.

Show exactly what you do.

One has been done for you.

$43 + 9 = 43 + \boxed{10} - \boxed{1} = \boxed{52}$

$57 + 9 = 57 + \boxed{\phantom{00}} - \boxed{\phantom{00}} = \boxed{\phantom{00}}$

$72 + 9 = 72 + \boxed{\phantom{00}} - \boxed{\phantom{00}} = \boxed{\phantom{00}}$

$38 - 9 = 38 - \boxed{\phantom{00}} + \boxed{\phantom{00}} = \boxed{\phantom{00}}$

1

**4.** Use **rounding** and **adjusting** to answer these.

Show exactly what you do.

One has been done for you.

$45 + 11 = 45 + \boxed{10} + \boxed{1} = \boxed{56}$

$38 + 11 = 38 + \boxed{\phantom{00}} + \boxed{\phantom{00}} = \boxed{\phantom{00}}$

$57 - 11 = 57 - \boxed{\phantom{00}} - \boxed{\phantom{00}} = \boxed{\phantom{00}}$

$76 - 11 = 76 - \boxed{\phantom{00}} - \boxed{\phantom{00}} = \boxed{\phantom{00}}$

1

Marks

**5.** Use a **mental calculation** strategy to answer these.

Show exactly what you do.

28 + 9 = 28 [  ] [  ] [  ] [  ] = [  ]

45 – 11 = 45 [  ] [  ] [  ] [  ] = [  ]

24 + 25 = 24 [  ] [  ] [  ] [  ] = [  ]

2

**6.** Suzie has 76 marbles.

Tom has nine more marbles than Suzie.

How many marbles does Tom have?

[                    marbles ]

1

Marks

**7.** Sejal has 64 stickers.

She gives **11** to George.

How many stickers does Sejal have left?

| | stickers |
|---|---|

1

**8.** Simon is thinking about the number **25**.

He **doubles** it.

Then **adds** 11.

What number does Simon end up with?

Show your working

2

End of test

1. Mark these calculations.

   Use a tick (✔) or a cross (✗).

|  | ✔ or ✗ |
|---|---|
| 36 + 15 = 15 + 36 | ☐ |
| 38 − 21 = 21 − 38 | ☐ |
| 57 + 23 = 23 + 57 | ☐ |
| 64 − 25 = 25 − 64 | ☐ |

1

2. Look at this bar model.

Write the **missing** number.

| 45 | |
|---|---|
| _____ | 21 |

1

Write the two **addition** calculations it shows.

☐ + ☐ = ☐

☐ + ☐ = ☐

1

Write the two **subtraction** calculations it shows.

☐ − ☐ = ☐

☐ − ☐ = ☐

1

3. The **difference** between 20 and 53 is **33**.

Marks

Write **two** more pairs of numbers with a difference of 33.

Show your working

Pair 1 _____ and _____

Pair 2 _____ and _____

1

4. Tia bakes **45** cupcakes for the school fair.

Lewis bakes **30**.

How many more cupcakes does Tia bake than Lewis?

cupcakes

1

How many cupcakes do they bake altogether?

cupcakes

1

Marks

5. Jagruti scores **45** points on the computer game.

William scores **23** points.

Aisha scores **18** points.

What is the **sum** of their scores?

| points |

1

6. Rosie has **23 more** shells than Sam.

Sam has **57** shells.

How many shells does Rosie have?

| shells |

1

How many shells do they have altogether?

| shells |

1

Marks

7. Write an **addition** calculation you could use to check that this subtraction calculation is correct.

$$38 - 11 = 27$$

☐ + ☐ = ☐

1

8. Complete the calculation.

Choose from these digits.

$$22 + ☐ = 91$$

End of test

1

**1.** Mika thinks of a number.

She **divides** it by **ten**.

Her answer is **six**.

What number is she thinking of?

Marks

1

**2.** Circle the **even** numbers.

43          18          97          68          36

1

Marks

**3.** Mark these calculations.

Use a tick (✔) or a cross (✗).

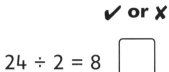

**✔ or ✗**

$$24 \div 2 = 8 \quad \square$$

$$5 \times 10 = 50 \quad \square$$

$$45 \div 5 = 9 \quad \square$$

$$7 \times 2 = 16 \quad \square$$

1

**4.** Write the missing numbers.

$$6 \times \boxed{\phantom{00}} = 12$$

$$\boxed{\phantom{00}} \times 5 = 40$$

$$24 \div \boxed{\phantom{00}} = 12$$

$$\boxed{\phantom{00}} \div 10 = 8$$

1

**5.** Alex thinks of a number.

He **multiplies** it by **five** and **doubles** it.

He ends up with **70**.

What number is Alex thinking of?

Marks

Show
your
working

2

**6.** 6 × 2 = 12

Use this fact to work out these.

60 × 2 = [ ]

60 × 20 = [ ]

30 × 20 = [ ]

30 × 40 = [ ]

2

End of test

Marks

1. Mark these calculations.

   Use a tick (✔) or a cross (✗).

   **✔ or ✗**

   $6 \times 5 = 5 \times 6$ ☐

   $60 \div 10 = 10 \div 60$ ☐

   $7 \times 3 = 3 \times 7$ ☐

   $35 \div 5 = 5 \div 35$ ☐

1

2. Here are some numbers.

   **3          21          7**

   Use these numbers to make **two multiplication** calculations.

   ☐ × ☐ = ☐

   ☐ × ☐ = ☐

1

   Use these numbers to make **two division** calculations.

   ☐ ÷ ☐ = ☐

   ☐ ÷ ☐ = ☐

1

Marks

**3.** Kris has **six** cubes.

Melanie has **ten times** as many.

How many cubes does Melanie have?

| | cubes |

1

**4.** Ben has **25** toy cars.

He shares them equally among **five** boxes.

How many cars are in each box?

| | cars |

1

Ben is given another **ten** toy cars.

He shares all the cars equally among the **five** boxes.

How many cars are in each box now?

Show your working

| | cars |

2

Marks

5. Judith has **four** books.

Carly has **five times** as many books as Judith.

How many **more** books does Carly have?

Show your working

| books |

2

How many books do they have **altogether**?

| books |

1

6. There are **five** packs of **ten** pencils and **six** single pencils.

How many pencils altogether?

| pencils |

1

End of test

Marks

1. Shade $\frac{1}{2}$ of each grid.

   Shade each grid in a different way.

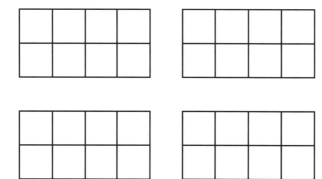

1

2. Shade $\frac{1}{4}$ on these clock faces.

   Shade each clock face in a different way.

1

**SCHOLASTIC Skills Test Papers**

**3.** Make these statements correct.

Marks

$$\frac{}{3} = 1$$

1

$$\frac{}{2} = 1$$

1

$$\frac{}{4} = 1$$

1

**4.** Tick the **smallest** fraction of the same whole.

Tick **one**.

$\frac{1}{2}$ ☐          $\frac{1}{3}$ ☐          $\frac{1}{4}$ ☐

1

**5.** Look at these faces.

What **fraction** is smiling?

Write the fraction in **two** different ways.

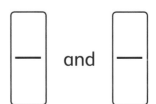 and

1

**6.** The whole bar represents **24**.

Shade $\frac{1}{2}$

| 24 | |
|---|---|
| | |

1

Write the value of $\frac{1}{2}$

1

Shade $\frac{1}{4}$

| 24 | |
|---|---|
| | |

1

Write the value of $\frac{1}{4}$

1

End of test

Marks

1. Complete the fraction.

$$\frac{1}{2} = \frac{}{4}$$

1

2. Complete the fraction.

$$\frac{1}{2} + \frac{}{4} = 1$$

1

3. Complete the fraction.

$$\frac{}{4} + \frac{1}{4} = \frac{3}{4}$$

1

Marks

**4.** Look at this bar.

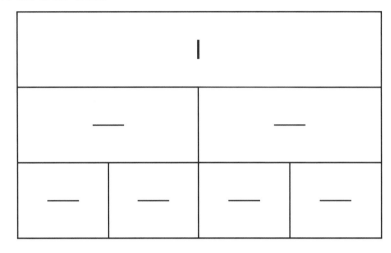

Write the **fractions** on the bar.

1

Use the bar to complete this statement.

$$\frac{3}{4} = \frac{1}{2} + \frac{\phantom{1}}{\phantom{1}}$$

1

**5.** Circle the shapes with **equivalent** parts shaded.

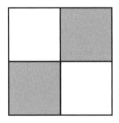 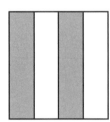 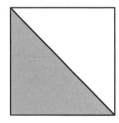

 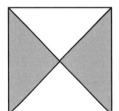 

2

**SCHOLASTIC** Skills Test Papers

**6.** Look at these fractions.

$$\frac{3}{4} \qquad \frac{1}{4} \qquad \frac{2}{4}$$

Use these fractions to make two **addition** calculations.

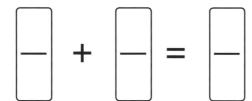

$$\boxed{\frac{\phantom{x}}{\phantom{x}}} + \boxed{\frac{\phantom{x}}{\phantom{x}}} = \boxed{\frac{\phantom{x}}{\phantom{x}}}$$

$$\boxed{\frac{\phantom{x}}{\phantom{x}}} + \boxed{\frac{\phantom{x}}{\phantom{x}}} = \boxed{\frac{\phantom{x}}{\phantom{x}}}$$

Use these fractions to make two **subtraction** calculations.

$$\boxed{\frac{\phantom{x}}{\phantom{x}}} - \boxed{\frac{\phantom{x}}{\phantom{x}}} = \boxed{\frac{\phantom{x}}{\phantom{x}}}$$

$$\boxed{\frac{\phantom{x}}{\phantom{x}}} - \boxed{\frac{\phantom{x}}{\phantom{x}}} = \boxed{\frac{\phantom{x}}{\phantom{x}}}$$

Marks

1

1

End of test

1. Write the **fraction** that is shaded.

Marks

—

1

2. What **fraction** is shaded?

—

1

Marks

3. Shade $\frac{1}{2}$ of each shape.

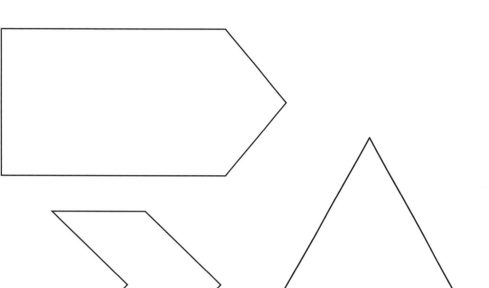

1

4. Shade $\frac{1}{4}$ of each shape.

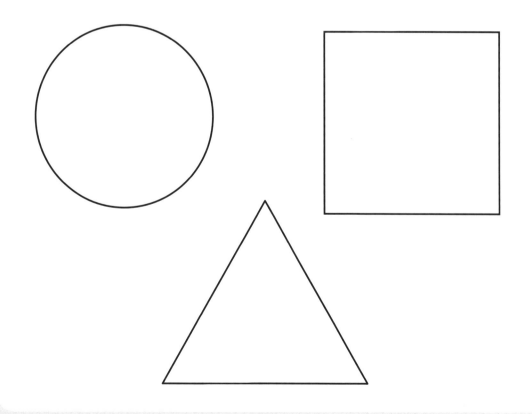

1

Marks

**5.** Tick the **two fractions** that show what area of the shape is shaded.

$\frac{1}{2}$ ☐          $\frac{1}{3}$ ☐

$\frac{1}{4}$ ☐          $\frac{2}{4}$ ☐          $\frac{3}{4}$ ☐

1

**6.** Look at this pattern.

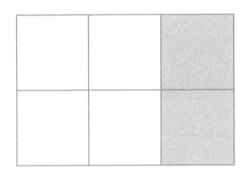

Circle the **fraction** that is shaded.

$\frac{1}{2}$     $\frac{1}{3}$     $\frac{1}{4}$     $\frac{2}{3}$     $\frac{2}{4}$     $\frac{3}{4}$

1

Shade **one more** square. What **fraction** is shaded now?

1

End of test

**SCHOLASTIC Skills Test Papers**

Marks

1. Shade $\frac{1}{2}$ of these circles.

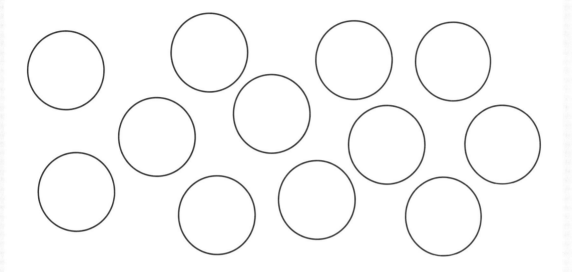

1

2. Shade $\frac{1}{4}$ of these triangles.

1

Marks

3. Draw a loop around $\frac{3}{4}$ of the paper clips.

1

4. Look at these strawberries.

Draw a loop around $\frac{1}{3}$ of the strawberries.

1

How many is $\frac{2}{3}$ of the strawberries?

| strawberries |

1

**5.** These are Finlay's construction bricks.

He gives $\frac{1}{3}$ of the bricks to Toby.

How many bricks does Finlay have left?

| bricks |

1

How many **more** bricks does Toby have than Finlay?

Show your working

| bricks |

2

**6.** Suzie shades some stars.

Circle the **fraction** that shows how many stars she shades.

$\frac{1}{2}$ $\frac{1}{3}$ $\frac{1}{4}$ $\frac{3}{4}$ $\frac{2}{4}$

1

End of test

1. The **whole** is **28**.

Write the value of $\frac{1}{2}$ in the parts.

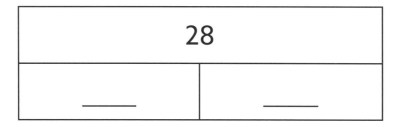

| 28 | |
|---|---|
| _____ | _____ |

1

2. Write $\frac{1}{3}$ of 21.

1

3. Jenny has **36** chews.

She eats $\frac{1}{2}$ of them.

How many does she eat?

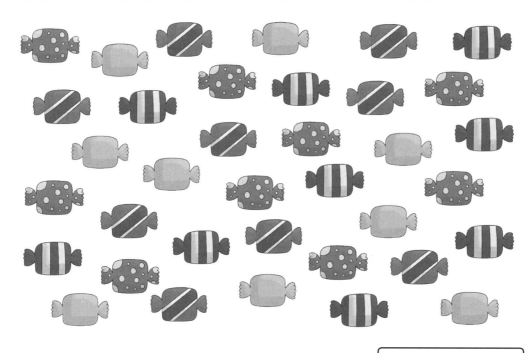

chews

1

**4.** Kenji has **21** football stickers.

He gives $\frac{1}{3}$ of them to Joe.

How many stickers does Kenji have left?

Marks

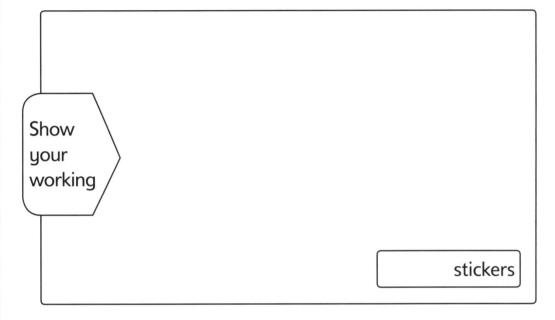

Show your working

stickers

2

**5.** Anna has a rope **80cm** long.

She cuts off a **quarter**.

What length of rope is left?

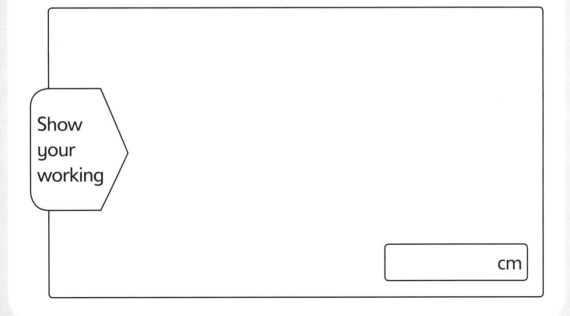

Show your working

cm

2

**6.** Harry has **39** stones.

Jake has **one third** of that number.

How many **more** stones does Harry have than Jake?

Show your working

stones

2

End of test

Marks

**1.** Complete the statements.

$$1m = \boxed{\phantom{xxxxxx}} cm$$

$$\tfrac{1}{2}m = \boxed{\phantom{xxxxxx}} cm$$

$$\tfrac{1}{4}m = \boxed{\phantom{xxxxxx}} cm$$

1

**2.** Complete the statement.

$$1m + \tfrac{1}{2}m = \boxed{\phantom{xxxxxx}} cm$$

1

**3.** Complete the statement.

$$275cm = 2m + \boxed{\underline{\phantom{xx}}\, m}$$

1

**4.** Measure these lines.

Marks

_____

| | cm |

_____

| | cm |

Compare the lengths.

Complete the boxes below.

1

| | < | |

| | > | |

Write a number statement to show how to make the lengths **equal**.

1

| | | | | | = | |

**5.** Emma has a piece of ribbon that is **1m 25cm** long.

Isla has a piece of ribbon that is **90cm** long.

1

How much **longer** is Emma's ribbon?

| | cm |

1

What is the **total** length of both pieces of ribbon?

| | m and | | cm |

**6.** Aaron is **1m 11cm** tall.

His father is **1m 80cm** tall.

How much **taller** than Aaron is his father?

|  cm |

Marks

1

Aaron's mother is **53cm** taller than Aaron.

How **tall** is Aaron's mother?

| m and  cm |

1

End of test

# 13: Mass and temperature

1. Write the **mass** of the pineapple.

g

1

2. Write the **temperature** the thermometer is showing.

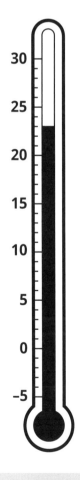

°C

1

Marks

3. Complete the statements.

1kg 250g = [ _____ ] g

2kg 600g = [ _____ ] g

3kg 750g = [ _____ ] g

1

4. Tom's dog weighs **5kg 700g**.

His cat weighs **2kg 300g**.

How much heavier is Tom's dog than his cat?

[ _____ kg _____ g ]

1

What is the **total** mass of the two animals?

[ _____ kg _____ g ]

1

Marks

**5.** Compare these temperatures.

Write **>** or **<**

$$25°C \boxed{\phantom{x}} 17°C$$
$$9°C \boxed{\phantom{x}} 13°C$$

1

**6.** At 6 o'clock in the **morning** the temperature was **9°C**.
It was **13 degrees** warmer by **noon**.

What temperature was it at noon?

$$\boxed{\phantom{xxxxxxxxxx}} °C$$

1

The temperature dropped **8°C** between noon and
6 o'clock in the **evening**.

What temperature was it at 6 o'clock in the evening?

$$\boxed{\phantom{xxxxxxxxxx}} °C$$

1

**7.** Look at these weighing scales.

Write the masses.

Oranges [                    ] g

Bananas [                    ] g

Potatoes [        kg            g ]

1

Compare the masses.

Write **>**, **<** or **=** in each box.

Bananas' mass [ ] Oranges' mass

Oranges' mass [ ] Potatoes' mass

Potatoes' mass [ ] Bananas' mass

1

Write the mass of the potatoes in **grams** only.

[                    ] g

1

End of test

Marks

1. Write the **capacity** of this measuring cylinder.

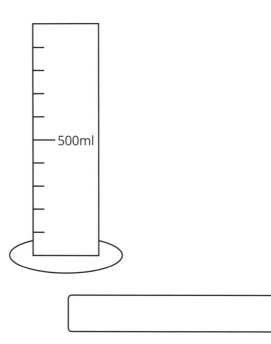

1

2. Write the **volume** of the water in this measuring cylinder.

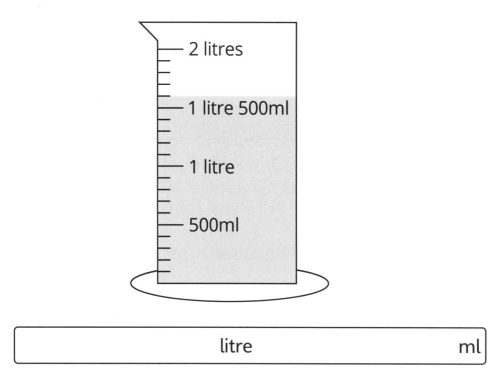

| litre | ml |

1

Marks

3. Complete the statements.

1400ml = [ litre         ml ]

2900ml = [ litres         ml ]

3200ml = [ litres         ml ]          1

4. Compare these **volumes**.

Write **>** or **<**.

1 litre 400ml [  ] 1200ml

2400ml [  ] 2 litres 800ml          1

5. Abdul buys a **1 litre** bottle of water.
   He drinks **750ml**.

What **volume** is left in Abdul's bottle?

[                    ml ]          1

Milo buys a **2 litre** bottle of water.
He drinks the same amount as Abdul.

What **volume** is left in Milo's bottle?

[ litre                ml ]          1

**6.** A farmer fills a bucket **half full** of water.

The bucket has a capacity of **5 litres**.

How much water is in the farmer's bucket?

Marks

| litres | ml |

1

The farmer uses some of the water to wash his muddy boots.

He has $\frac{1}{2}$ litre left.

How much water did the farmer use to wash his boots?

| | l |

1

**End of test**

Marks

1. Omar has these coins.

How much money does he have?

£ _____

1

2. Order these amounts from **least** to **greatest** value.

10p          20p          £1          1p          50p

least
value

greatest
value

[ ]   [ ]   [ ]   [ ]   [ ]

1

3. Jade buys a glass of milk and a cookie.

65p                              45p

How much does she spend?

£ _____

1

4. Ethan buys a comic and a pack of crayons.

Marks

£1.25

£2.60

How much does he spend?

£ [        ]

1

What is his change from £5?

£ [        ]

1

**5.** This is Sadie's purse.

Marks

How much money does Sadie have?

£ [          ]

1

Chloe has £1.20 more than Sadie.

How much money does Chloe have?

£ [          ]

1

**6.** Ben saves £1.50 each week for **five** weeks.

How much does he save over the **five** weeks?

£ [          ]

1

Jack saves **twice** as much money over the **five** weeks.

How much does Jack save?

£ [          ]

1

End of test

Marks

**1.** Write the time showing on the clock.

1

**2.** What time is this clock showing?

1

**Marks**

3. Write the day that is **two** days after Tuesday.

1

4. Anya's watch is **ten** minutes fast.

Draw the correct time on this watch face below.

1

Marks

5. Ellie went to play with her friend.
   She arrived at her friend's house at **20 minutes past 4**.
   She left her friend's house at **quarter past 6**.

Draw the **two** times on these clocks.

20 minutes past 4                    quarter past 6                    2

How long was Ellie at her friend's house?

[                                                    ]                  1

6. Marcel played football for **50** minutes.
   Luke played football for **35** minutes.

For how much longer did Marcel play football?

[                              minutes]                                 1

What is the **total** time the boys spent playing football?

[          hours and                minutes]                            1

End of test

Marks

1. What **shape** are the faces of this cube?

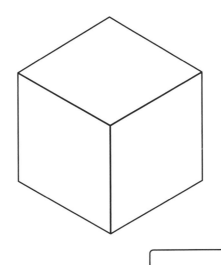

1

2. Tick the **pyramids**.

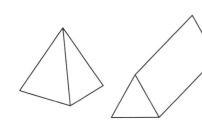 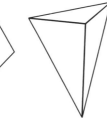  

1

3. Use the words **face**, **edge** and **vertex** to label the parts of the **triangular prism**.

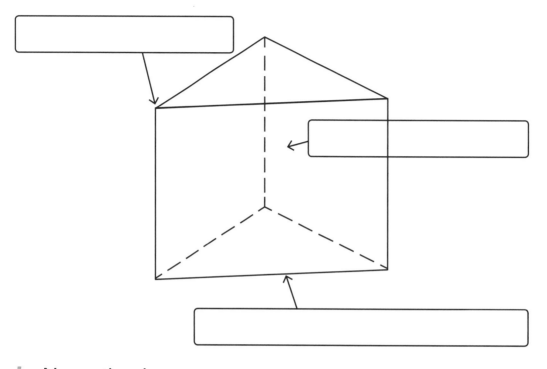

1

4. Name the shapes.

Write your answers in the table.

| Shape | Number of faces | Number of edges | Number of vertices |
|---|---|---|---|
| | 6 | 12 | 8 |
| | 5 | 9 | 6 |
| | 5 | 8 | 5 |

1

5. Reena is thinking of a **3D** shape.

It has **one** curved surface and **two** circular faces.

What shape is she thinking of?

Marks

1

6. Lucy builds a tower using **3D** shapes.

Label the shapes she uses.

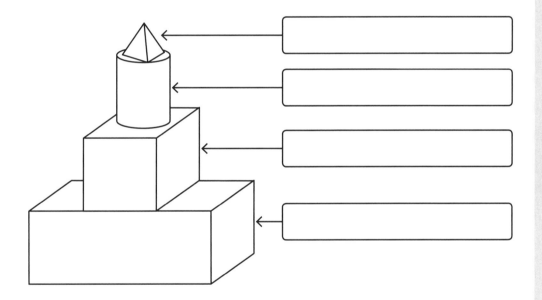

2

End of test

Marks

1. Draw lines to match each shape to its name.

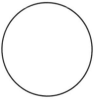

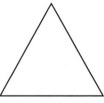

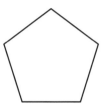

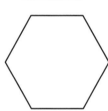

hexagon

triangle

circle

pentagon

1

2. Tick the **triangles**.

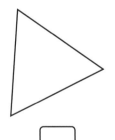

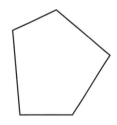

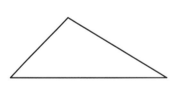

☐        ☐        ☐

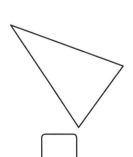

☐        ☐        ☐

1

**3.** Tick the **quadrilaterals**.

Marks

**4.** Draw **two** lines of symmetry on this rectangle.

1

1

**5.** Complete the table.

| Shape | Number of sides | Number of corners |
|---|---|---|
| _____ | 3 | 3 |
| Rectangle | _____ | 4 |
| Pentagon | 5 | _____ |
| _____ | 6 | _____ |

2

**6.** Alex draws a symmetrical man using different shapes.

Label the shapes he uses.

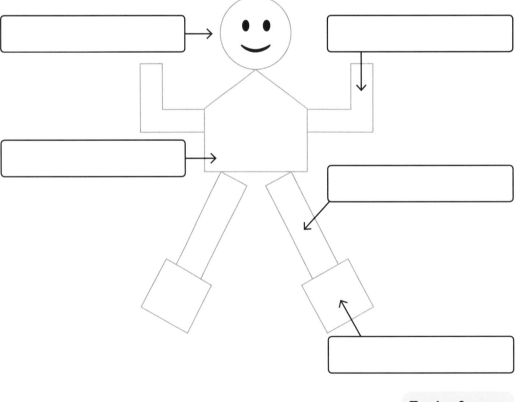

2

End of test

Marks

1. Use these words to describe the **position** of the **cat**.

between     underneath     beside

The cat is _____ the mice.

The cat is _____ the mice.

The cat is _____ the mice.

1

2. Tick the arrows that show **half** a turn.

1

Marks

3. Circle the figure's **left** leg.

1

4. Complete the statement.

$\frac{1}{4}$ turn + $\boxed{\underline{\phantom{--}} \text{ turn}}$ = whole turn

1

Marks

**5.** This is a dial with a marker.

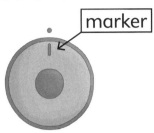

Draw a new marker on each dial below to show the following turns in a **clockwise** direction.

A **quarter** turn

A **three-quarter** turn

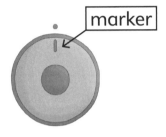

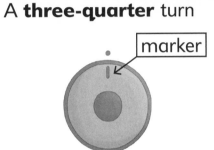

2

**6.** Kamal is facing the door.

He thinks that if he makes a $\frac{1}{2}$ turn in a **clockwise** direction he will be in the same position that he would be in if he made a $\frac{1}{2}$ turn in an **anticlockwise** direction.

Is he correct? Explain your thinking.

1

End of test

Marks

1. What **number** does this tally represent?

IIII IIII IIII IIII IIII

1

2. This table shows Class 2's favourite fruit.

| Fruit | Number of children |
|---|---|
| Orange | 12 |
| Peach | 4 |
| Apple | 10 |
| Pear | 2 |
| Grapes | 15 |

What is the most popular fruit?

1

Marks

3. Complete the table.

| Favourite colour | Tally | Number of children |
|---|---|---|
| Red | ЖЖ ЖЖ IIII | |
| Blue | | 12 |
| Yellow | | 6 |
| Orange | ЖЖ | |
| Green | | 3 |

2

4. This diagram shows children's favourite animals.

| Animal | Number of children who chose it |
|---|---|
| Lion | ●●●●●● |
| Monkey | ●●●●● |
| Elephant | ●●●◖ |
| Giraffe | ●●● |
| Hippo | ● |

● = **two** children

How many **more** children like lions than hippos?

[ ] children

1

How many **fewer** children like giraffes than monkeys?

[ ] children

1

**5.** Jamie does a survey to find out what types of television programmes his family and friends like to watch.

This chart shows his results.

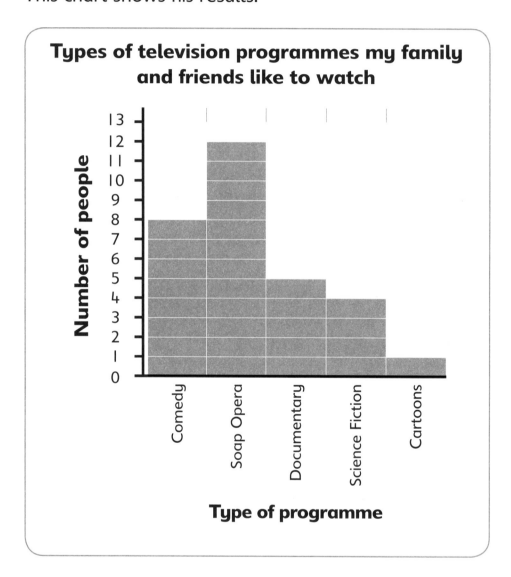

How many more people like comedy than documentary?

people

How many people took part in the survey?

people

**6.** Alicia made this table to show her friends' favourite colours.

| | |
|---|---|
| Green | 8 |
| Red | 9 |
| Blue | 12 |
| Yellow | 5 |

She then drew a pictogram.

| Colour | Number of children who chose it |
|---|---|
| Green | ● ● ● |
| Red | ● ● ● ● ◖ |
| Blue | ● ● ● ● ● ● |
| Yellow | ● ● |

● = **two** children

Some information is missing.

Add it to the pictogram.

1

Marks

7. This table shows the sports that **30** people like to watch on television.

**Draw** the tally marks in the table.

| Sport | Number of people who chose it | Tally |
|---|---|---|
| Football | 13 | |
| Athletics | 8 | |
| Formula One | 4 | |
| Tennis | 4 | |
| Cricket | 1 | |

1

More people like athletics than tennis.

How many more?

[                    people]

1

Three people responded to the survey late.

They all said they like tennis.

How many more people like athletics than tennis now?

Show your working

[                    people]

2

End of test

# Answers

The answers are given below. They are referenced by page number and question number. The answers usually only include the information the children are expected to give. There may be some places where the answers vary or multiple answers are acceptable, these are marked as such. Note that in some places, answers will be varied and subjective from child to child, and a fair degree of marker discretion and interpretation is needed, particularly if children's understanding and skills have to be deduced from their answers.

| Question | Answers | Marks |
|---|---|---|
| | **NUMBER** | |
| | **1: Counting and representing number (pages 8–10)** | |
| 1 | 15, 25, 30, 35 | 1 |
| 2 | 98 | 1 |
| | 90     100 | 1 |
| 3 | 50, 48, 44, 42 | 1 |
| 4 | Accept any drawing that represents 63. Expect children to be able to explain their drawing if it is unclear. | 1 |
| 5 | 90, 150, 180, 210<br>**Award 1 mark** for 4 correct answers. **Award 1 mark** for 3 answers correct. | 2 |
| 6 | 54  56<br>64  65  66<br>74  76<br>**Award 2 marks** for 6 correct answers. **Award 1 mark** for 4 or 5 answers correct. | 2 |
| | **2: Comparing and ordering numbers (pages 11–13)** | |
| 1 | For example:<br>50 + 9; 40 + 19; 30 + 29; 20 + 39; 10 + 49 | 1 |
| 2 | 83, 79, 68, 23, 16 | 1 |
| 3 | Tens or 5 tens or 50 | 1 |
| | Ones or 8 ones or 8 | 1 |
| 4 | 87 | 1 |
| | Possible explanation: 8 is the greatest number in the 10s position | 1 |
| 5 | 43 **<** 98; 30 + 4 **=** 20 + 14; 87 **>** 37 | 1 |
| 6 | 80<br>**Award 2 marks** for correct answer of 80. **Award 1 mark** for evidence that Anya's number is 63. | 2 |
| | **ADDITION AND SUBTRACTION** | |
| | **3: Adding and subtracting mentally (pages 14–17)** | |
| 1 | 58 + 2 + 5 = 65<br>76 + 4 + 1 = 81<br>64 − 4 − 1 = 59 | 1 |
| 2 | 25 + 25 + 1 = 51<br>32 + 32 + 1 = 65<br>41 + 41 + 1 = 83 | 1 |
| 3 | 57 + 10 − 1 = 66<br>72 + 10 − 1 = 81<br>38 − 10 + 1 = 29 | 1 |
| 4 | 38 + 10 + 1 = 49<br>57 − 10 − 1 = 46<br>76 − 10 − 1 = 65 | 1 |

| Question | Answers | Marks |
|---|---|---|
| 5 | 28 + 10 − 1 = 37 or 28 + 2 + 7 = 37<br>45 − 10 − 1 = 34<br>24 + 24 + 1 = 49 or 25 + 25 −1 = 49<br>**Award 2 marks** for 3 correct answers. **Award 1 mark** for 2 correct answers. | 2 |
| 6 | 85 marbles | 1 |
| 7 | 53 stickers | 1 |
| 8 | 61<br>Award **2 marks** for correct answer. Allow **1 mark** for evidence that shows double 25 is 50. | 2 |

### 4: Inverse operations (pages 18–21)

| Question | Answers | Marks |
|---|---|---|
| 1 | 36 + 15 = 15 + 36 ✓<br>38 − 21 = 21 − 38 ✗<br>57 + 23 = 23 + 57 ✓<br>64 − 25 = 25 − 64 ✗ | 1 |
| 2 | 24 | 1 |
|  | 21 + 24 = 45 and 24 + 21 = 45 | 1 |
|  | 45 − 21 = 24 and 45 − 24 = 21 | 1 |
| 3 | Any two pairs of numbers that have a difference of 33. For example: 30 and 63; 40 and 73; 10 and 43 | 1 |
| 4 | 15 cupcakes | 1 |
|  | 75 cupcakes | 1 |
| 5 | 86 points | 1 |
| 6 | 80 shells | 1 |
|  | 137 shells | 1 |
| 7 | 27 + 11 = 38 or 11 + 27 = 38 | 1 |
| 8 | 69 | 1 |

## MULTIPLICATION AND DIVISION

### 5: Multiplying and dividing mentally (pages 22–24)

| Question | Answers | Marks |
|---|---|---|
| 1 | 60 | 1 |
| 2 | 18, 68, 36 | 1 |
| 3 | 24 ÷ 2 = 8 ✗<br>5 × 10 = 50 ✓<br>45 ÷ 5 = 9 ✓<br>7 × 2 = 16 ✗ | 1 |
| 4 | 2<br>8<br>2<br>80 | 1 |
| 5 | 7<br>**Award 2 marks** for correct answer of 7. **Award 1 mark** for evidence of correct working, such as halving 70 to get 35 and dividing 35 by 5, but with one mistake in the calculation. | 2 |
| 6 | 120<br>1200<br>600<br>1200<br>**Award 2 marks** for all 4 answers correct. **Award 1 mark** for 3 answers correct. | 2 |

### 6: Problem solving with multiplication and division (pages 25–27)

| Question | Answers | Marks |
|---|---|---|
| 1 | 6 × 5 = 5 × 6 ✓<br>60 ÷ 10 = 10 ÷ 60 ✗<br>7 × 3 = 3 × 7 ✓<br>35 ÷ 5 = 5 ÷ 35 ✗ | 1 |
| 2 | 3 × 7 = 21; 7 × 3 = 21 | 1 |
|  | 21 ÷ 7 = 3; 21 ÷ 3 = 7 | 1 |

**SCHOLASTIC Skills Test Papers**

| Question | Answers | Marks |
|---|---|---|
| 3 | 60 cubes | 1 |
| 4 | 5 cars | 1 |
| | 7 cars<br>**Award 1 mark** for correct answer of 7 cars. **Award 1 mark** for evidence of correct working, for example: adding 10 to 25 and then dividing by 5, but resulting in the wrong answer. | 2 |
| 5 | 16 books<br>**Award 2 marks** for correct answer of 16 books. Allow **1 mark** for evidence of correct working: $4 \times 5 = 20$, and $20 - 4 = 16$, but with one arithmetical error. | 2 |
| | 24 books | 1 |
| 6 | 56 pencils | 1 |

FRACTIONS

### 7: Fractions (pages 28–30)

| Question | Answers | Marks |
|---|---|---|
| 1 | Any four squares shaded on each grid. Each grid must be shaded differently to award the mark. | 1 |
| 2 | Any 15-minute period shaded. Each clock face must be shaded differently to award the mark. | 1 |
| 3 | 3 | 1 |
| | 2 | 1 |
| | 4 | 1 |
| 4 | $\frac{1}{4}$ | 1 |
| 5 | $\frac{1}{2}$ and $\frac{2}{4}$ | 1 |
| 6 | <br>12 | 1<br><br>1 |
| | <br>6 | 1<br><br>1 |

### 8: Equivalent fractions (pages 31–33)

| Question | Answers | Marks |
|---|---|---|
| 1 | 2 | 1 |
| 2 | 2 | 1 |
| 3 | 2 | 1 |
| 4 | | 1 |
| | $\frac{1}{4}$ | 1 |
| 5 | <br>**Award 2 marks** if all 4 correct shapes are chosen. **Award 1 mark** if 1, 2 or 3 correct shapes are chosen. | 2 |
| 6 | $\frac{1}{4} + \frac{2}{4} = \frac{3}{4}$<br>$\frac{2}{4} + \frac{1}{4} = \frac{3}{4}$ | 1 |
| 6 | $\frac{3}{4} - \frac{2}{4} = \frac{1}{4}$<br>$\frac{3}{4} - \frac{1}{4} = \frac{2}{4}$ | 1 |

| Question | Answers | Marks |
|:---:|:---|:---:|
| | **9: Fractions of shapes (pages 34–36)** | |
| 1 | $\frac{1}{3}$ | 1 |
| 2 | $\frac{1}{2}$ or $\frac{2}{4}$ | 1 |
| 3 | <br>The equilateral triangle can be halved in three directions from corner to midpoint on side. | 1 |
| 4 | <br>The square could also be quartered diagonally from corner to corner. | 1 |
| 5 | $\frac{1}{2}$ and $\frac{2}{4}$ ticked | 1 |
| 6 | $\frac{1}{3}$ | 1 |
| | $\frac{1}{2}$ Some children may answer $\frac{3}{6}$ which is also correct, though children are not introduced to sixths until Year 3. Note that it is not important which square they shade. | 1 |
| | **10: Fractions of sets of objects (pages 37–39)** | |
| 1 | 6 circles shaded | 1 |
| 2 | 5 triangles shaded | 1 |
| 3 | A loop around 9 paper clips | 1 |
| 4 | A loop around 6 strawberries | 1 |
| | 12 strawberries | 1 |
| 5 | 18 bricks | 1 |
| | 9 bricks<br>**Award 2 marks** for correct answer. **Award 1 mark** for evidence of correct working: Toby has 18 bricks, Finlay has 9 bricks, 18 − 9 = 9, but with one error. | 2 |
| 6 | $\frac{1}{2}$ | 1 |
| | **11: Fractions of quantities (pages 40–42)** | |
| 1 | <table><tr><td colspan="2" align="center">28</td></tr><tr><td>14</td><td>14</td></tr></table> | 1 |
| 2 | 7 | 1 |
| 3 | 18 chews | 1 |
| 4 | 14 stickers<br>**Award 2 marks** for correct answer of 14. **Award 1 mark** for evidence of finding $\frac{1}{3}$ of 21 is 7, 21 − 7 = 14 or $\frac{2}{3}$ of 21 is 14. | 2 |
| 5 | 60cm<br>**Award 2 marks** for correct answer of 60. **Award 1 mark** for evidence of finding $\frac{1}{4}$ of 80 and an attempt to subtract this from 80. | 2 |
| 6 | 26 stones<br>**Award 2 marks** for correct answer of 26. **Award 1 mark** for evidence that Harry has 39 stones and Jake has 13, and an attempt to subtract 13 from 39 but with one error. | 2 |
| | **MEASUREMENT** | |
| | **12: Length (pages 43–45)** | |
| 1 | 100<br>50<br>25 | 1 |
| 2 | 150cm | 1 |
| 3 | $\frac{3}{4}$ m | 1 |

| Question | Answers | Marks |
|---|---|---|
| 4 | 10cm < 14cm; 14cm > 10cm | 1 |
| | 10cm + 4cm = 14cm   or   14cm − 4cm = 10cm | 1 |
| 5 | 35cm | 1 |
| | 2m 15cm or 215cm | 1 |
| 6 | 69cm | 1 |
| | 1m 64cm | 1 |

### 13: Mass and temperature (pages 46–49)

| Question | Answers | Marks |
|---|---|---|
| 1 | 750g | 1 |
| 2 | 23°C | 1 |
| 3 | 1250<br>2600<br>3750 | 1 |
| 4 | 3kg 400g | 1 |
| | 8kg | 1 |
| 5 | 25°C > 17°C<br>9°C < 13°C | 1 |
| 6 | 22°C | 1 |
| | 14°C | 1 |
| 7 | Oranges: 450g<br>Bananas: 700g<br>Potatoes: 3kg 500g | 1 |
| | ><br><<br>> | 1 |
| | 3500g | 1 |

### 14: Capacity and volume (pages 50–52)

| Question | Answers | Marks |
|---|---|---|
| 1 | 1 litre | 1 |
| 2 | 1 litre 600ml | 1 |
| 3 | 1 litre 400ml<br>2 litres 900ml<br>3 litres 200ml | 1 |
| 4 | 1 litre 400ml > 1,200ml<br>2400ml < 2 litres 800ml | 1 |
| 5 | 250ml | 1 |
| | 1 litre 250ml or 1250ml | 1 |
| 6 | 2 litres 500ml or 2500ml | 1 |
| | 2 litres | 1 |

### 15: Money (pages 53–55)

| Question | Answers | Marks |
|---|---|---|
| 1 | £1.77 | 1 |
| 2 | 1p, 10p, 20p, 50p, £1 | 1 |
| 3 | £1.10 | 1 |
| 4 | £3.85 | 1 |
| | £1.15 | 1 |
| 5 | £4.72 | 1 |
| | £5.92 | 1 |
| 6 | £7.50 | 1 |
| | £15 | 1 |

### 16: Time (pages 56–58)

| Question | Answers | Marks |
|---|---|---|
| 1 | 25 minutes past 10 or 10:25 | 1 |
| 2 | 25 minutes to 3 or 2:35 or 35 minutes past 2 | 1 |

| Question | Answers | Marks |
|---|---|---|
| 3 | Thursday | 1 |
| 4 | | 1 |
| 5 |  Award 1 mark for each correct clock. | 2 |
| | 1 hour 55 minutes | 1 |
| 6 | 15 minutes | 1 |
| | 1 hour 25 minutes | 1 |

**17: 3D shapes (pages 59–61)**

| Question | Answers | Marks |
|---|---|---|
| 1 | Square | 1 |
| 2 | A tick below shapes 1, 3 and 4 | 1 |
| 3 | | 1 |

| Shape | Number of faces | Number of edges | Number of vertices |
|---|---|---|---|
| **Cube** or **cuboid** | 6 | 12 | 8 |
| **Triangular prism** | 5 | 9 | 6 |
| **Pyramid (square based)** | 5 | 8 | 5 |

(Question 4, Marks: 1)

| Question | Answers | Marks |
|---|---|---|
| 5 | Cylinder | 1 |
| 6 |  Award 2 marks for all 4 correct. Award 1 mark for 3 correct.' | 2 |

**18: 2D shapes (pages 62–64)**

| Question | Answers | Marks |
|---|---|---|
| 1 | | 1 |

| Question | Answers | Marks |
|---|---|---|
| 2 | ✓    ✓    ✓ | 1 |
| 3 | ✓    ✓ | 1 |
| 4 | | 1 |
| 5 | (see table below) | 2 |

| Shape | Number of sides | Number of corners |
|---|---|---|
| **Triangle** | 3 | 3 |
| Rectangle | **4** | 4 |
| Pentagon | 5 | **5** |
| **Hexagon** | 6 | **6** |

**Award 2 marks** for all 5 correct. **Award 1 mark** for 3 or 4 correct.

| Question | Answers | Marks |
|---|---|---|
| 6 | circle → hexagon; pentagon → ; rectangle; square | 2 |

**Award 2 marks** for all 5 correct. **Award 1 mark** for 3 or 4 correct.

### GEOMETRY – POSITION AND DIRECTION

#### 19: Turns (pages 65–67)

| Question | Answers | Marks |
|---|---|---|
| 1 | The cat is **underneath** the mice.<br>The cat is **beside** the mice.<br>The cat is **between** the mice. | 1 |
| 2 | ✓    ✓ | 1 |
| 3 | | 1 |
| 4 | $\frac{3}{4}$ turn | 1 |

| Question | Answers | Marks |
|---|---|---|
| 5 | <br>**Award 1 mark** for each correct marker. | 2 |
| 6 | Kamal is correct. Accept diagrams as an explanation. | 1 |

### STATISTICS
### 20: Charts and tables (pages 68–72)

| Question | Answers | Marks |
|---|---|---|
| 1 | 24 | 1 |
| 2 | Grapes | 1 |

| Favourite colour | Tally | Number of children |
|---|---|---|
| Red | ⊞⊞ ⊞⊞ IIIII | **14** |
| Blue | ⊞⊞ ⊞⊞ II | 12 |
| Yellow | ⊞⊞ I | 6 |
| Orange | ⊞⊞ | **5** |
| Green | III | 3 |

3 — **Award 2 marks** for all 5 answers correct. **Award 1 mark** for 3 or 4 answers correct. — 2

| Question | Answers | Marks |
|---|---|---|
| 4 | 10 children (12 – 2) | 1 |
|  | 4 children (10 – 6) | 1 |
| 5 | 3 people (8 – 5) | 1 |
|  | 30 people (8 + 12 + 5 + 4 + 1) | 1 |

| Colour | Number of children who chose it |
|---|---|
| Green | ● ● ● ● |
| Red | ● ● ● ● ◖ |
| Blue | ● ● ● ● ● ● |
| Yellow | ● ● ◖ |

6 — 1

| Sport | Number of people who chose it | Tally |
|---|---|---|
| Football | 13 | ⊞⊞ ⊞⊞ III |
| Athletics | 8 | ⊞⊞ III |
| Formula One | 4 | IIII |
| Tennis | 4 | IIII |
| Cricket | 1 | I |

7 — 1

| Answers | Marks |
|---|---|
| 4 people (8 – 4) | 1 |
| 1<br>**Award 2 marks** for correct answer of 1. **Award 1 mark** for some indication that 4 + 3 = 7 who like tennis, 8 – 7 = 1, but with one error. | 2 |

**SCHOLASTIC Skills Test Papers**

# Answer grids

NUMBER AND PLACE VALUE

NUMBER AND PLACE VALUE

### Skills Test Paper 1: Counting and representing number

| Q | Possible marks | Actual marks | Workbook links |
|---|---|---|---|
| 1 | 1 | | |
| 2 | 2 | | |
| 3 | 1 | | |
| 4 | 1 | | 6–8 |
| 5 | 2 | | |
| 6 | 2 | | |
| Total | 9 | | |

### Skills Test Paper 2: Comparing and ordering numbers

| Q | Possible marks | Actual marks | Workbook links |
|---|---|---|---|
| 1 | 1 | | |
| 2 | 1 | | |
| 3 | 2 | | |
| 4 | 2 | | 9–11 |
| 5 | 1 | | |
| 6 | 2 | | |
| Total | 9 | | |

NUMBER – ADDITION AND SUBTRACTION

### Skills Test Paper 3: Adding and subtracting mentally

| Q | Possible marks | Actual marks | Workbook links |
|---|---|---|---|
| 1 | 1 | | |
| 2 | 1 | | |
| 3 | 1 | | |
| 4 | 1 | | |
| 5 | 2 | | 12–14 |
| 6 | 1 | | |
| 7 | 1 | | |
| 8 | 2 | | |
| Total | 10 | | |

# Answer grids

**Skills Test Paper 4: Inverse operations**

| Q | Possible marks | Actual marks | Workbook links |
|---|---|---|---|
| 1 | 1 | | |
| 2 | 3 | | |
| 3 | 1 | | |
| 4 | 2 | | |
| 5 | 1 | | 15–17 |
| 6 | 2 | | |
| 7 | 1 | | |
| 8 | 1 | | |
| Total | 12 | | |

NUMBER – MULTIPLICATION AND DIVISION

**Skills Test Paper 5: Multiplying and dividing mentally**

| Q | Possible marks | Actual marks | Workbook links |
|---|---|---|---|
| 1 | 1 | | |
| 2 | 1 | | |
| 3 | 1 | | |
| 4 | 1 | | 18–20 |
| 5 | 2 | | |
| 6 | 2 | | |
| Total | 8 | | |

**Skills Test Paper 6: Problem solving with multiplication and division**

| Q | Possible marks | Actual marks | Workbook links |
|---|---|---|---|
| 1 | 1 | | |
| 2 | 2 | | |
| 3 | 1 | | |
| 4 | 3 | | 21–22 |
| 5 | 3 | | |
| 6 | 1 | | |
| Total | 11 | | |

FRACTIONS

**Skills Test Paper 7: Fractions**

| Q | Possible marks | Actual marks | Workbook links |
|---|---|---|---|
| 1 | 1 | | |
| 2 | 1 | | |
| 3 | 3 | | |
| 4 | 1 | | 23–25 |
| 5 | 1 | | |
| 6 | 4 | | |
| Total | 11 | | |

**Skills Test Paper 8: Equivalent fractions**

| Q | Possible marks | Actual marks | Workbook links |
|---|---|---|---|
| 1 | 1 | | |
| 2 | 1 | | |
| 3 | 1 | | |
| 4 | 2 | | 26–27 |
| 5 | 2 | | |
| 6 | 2 | | |
| Total | 9 | | |

**Skills Test Paper 9: Fractions of shapes**

| Q | Possible marks | Actual marks | Workbook links |
|---|---|---|---|
| 1 | 1 | | |
| 2 | 1 | | |
| 3 | 1 | | |
| 4 | 1 | | 28–29 |
| 5 | 1 | | |
| 6 | 2 | | |
| Total | 7 | | |

# Answer grids

### Skills Test Paper 10: Fractions of sets of objects

| Q | Possible marks | Actual marks | Workbook links |
|---|---|---|---|
| 1 | 1 | | |
| 2 | 1 | | |
| 3 | 1 | | |
| 4 | 2 | | 30–31 |
| 5 | 3 | | |
| 6 | 1 | | |
| Total | 9 | | |

### Skills Test Paper 11: Fractions of quantities

| Q | Possible marks | Actual marks | Workbook links |
|---|---|---|---|
| 1 | 1 | | |
| 2 | 1 | | |
| 3 | 1 | | |
| 4 | 2 | | 32–33 |
| 5 | 2 | | |
| 6 | 2 | | |
| Total | 9 | | |

MEASUREMENT

### Skills Test Paper 12: Length

| Q | Possible marks | Actual marks | Workbook links |
|---|---|---|---|
| 1 | 1 | | |
| 2 | 1 | | |
| 3 | 1 | | |
| 4 | 2 | | 34–36 |
| 5 | 2 | | |
| 6 | 2 | | |
| Total | 9 | | |

### Skills Test Paper 13: Mass and temperature

| Q | Possible marks | Actual marks | Workbook links |
|---|---|---|---|
| 1 | 1 | | |
| 2 | 1 | | |
| 3 | 1 | | |
| 4 | 2 | | 37–39 |
| 5 | 1 | | |
| 6 | 2 | | |
| 7 | 3 | | |
| Total | 11 | | |

### Skills Test Paper 14: Capacity and volume

| Q | Possible marks | Actual marks | Workbook links |
|---|---|---|---|
| 1 | 1 | | |
| 2 | 1 | | |
| 3 | 1 | | |
| 4 | 1 | | 40–42 |
| 5 | 2 | | |
| 6 | 2 | | |
| Total | 8 | | |

### Skills Test Paper 15: Money

| Q | Possible marks | Actual marks | Workbook links |
|---|---|---|---|
| 1 | 1 | | |
| 2 | 1 | | |
| 3 | 1 | | |
| 4 | 2 | | 43–45 |
| 5 | 2 | | |
| 6 | 2 | | |
| Total | 9 | | |

# Answer grids

**Skills Test Paper 16: Time**

| Q | Possible marks | Actual marks | Workbook links |
|---|---|---|---|
| 1 | 1 | | |
| 2 | 1 | | |
| 3 | 1 | | |
| 4 | 1 | | 46–48 |
| 5 | 3 | | |
| 6 | 2 | | |
| Total | 9 | | |

GEOMETRY – PROPERTIES OF SHAPE

**Skills Test Paper 17: 3D shapes**

| Q | Possible marks | Actual marks | Workbook links |
|---|---|---|---|
| 1 | 1 | | |
| 2 | 1 | | |
| 3 | 1 | | |
| 4 | 1 | | 49–50 |
| 5 | 1 | | |
| 6 | 2 | | |
| Total | 7 | | |

**Skills Test Paper 18: 2D shapes**

| Q | Possible marks | Actual marks | Workbook links |
|---|---|---|---|
| 1 | 1 | | |
| 2 | 1 | | |
| 3 | 1 | | |
| 4 | 1 | | 51–52 |
| 5 | 2 | | |
| 6 | 2 | | |
| Total | 8 | | |

GEOMETRY – POSITION AND DIRECTION

**Skills Test Paper 19: Turns**

| Q | Possible marks | Actual marks | Workbook links |
|---|---|---|---|
| 1 | 1 | | |
| 2 | 1 | | |
| 3 | 1 | | |
| 4 | 1 | | 53–55 |
| 5 | 2 | | |
| 6 | 1 | | |
| Total | 7 | | |

STATISTICS

**Skills Test Paper 20: Charts and tables**

| Q | Possible marks | Actual marks | Workbook links |
|---|---|---|---|
| 1 | 1 | | |
| 2 | 1 | | |
| 3 | 2 | | |
| 4 | 2 | | 56–59 |
| 5 | 2 | | |
| 6 | 1 | | |
| 7 | 4 | | |
| Total | 13 | | |

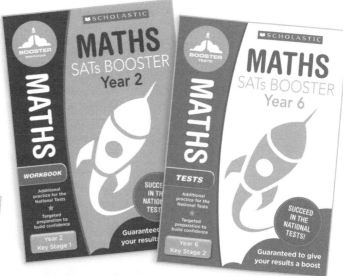

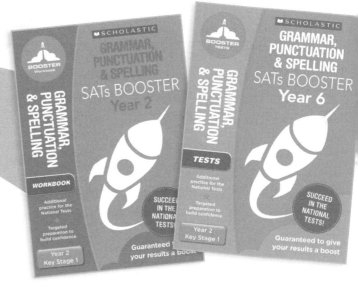

# SCHOLASTIC

# MATHS

## SATs CHALLENGE

## YEAR 2

**Workbook**

FOR CHILDREN WORKING AT GREATER DEPTH

Scholastic Education, an imprint of Scholastic Ltd

Book End, Range Road, Witney, Oxfordshire, OX29 0YD

Registered office: Westfield Road, Southam, Warwickshire CV47 0RA

www.scholastic.co.uk

**British Library Cataloguing-in-Publication Data**

A catalogue record for this book is available from the British Library.

**ISBN 978-1407-17540-9**

Printed and bound by Ashford Colour Press

**Author** Caroline Clissold

**Editorial** Rachel Morgan, Shannon Keenlyside, Audrey Stokes, Julia Roberts, Jackie Mace

**Cover and Series Design** Neil Salt and Nicolle Thomas

**Layout** Claire Green

**Illustration** Adam Linley/Beehive Illustration; illustration of marbles and illustration of shell p17 Tom Heard/The Bright Agency

**Technical artwork** Claire Green

# Contents

# How to use this book

This *Workbook* helps you to check what you already know, practise what you've learned and challenge yourself to fly higher!

You can work through all of the activities in order or you can dip in and out to brush up your skills or explore in more depth. Use the progress chart opposite to record which skills you've checked and practised. Aim higher by having a go at the questions in the *Skills Test Papers*.

You can check the answers at the back of the book.

What you should be able to do after you complete the skills check and practice questions. You can tick off each one as you can do it.

The title of the topic.

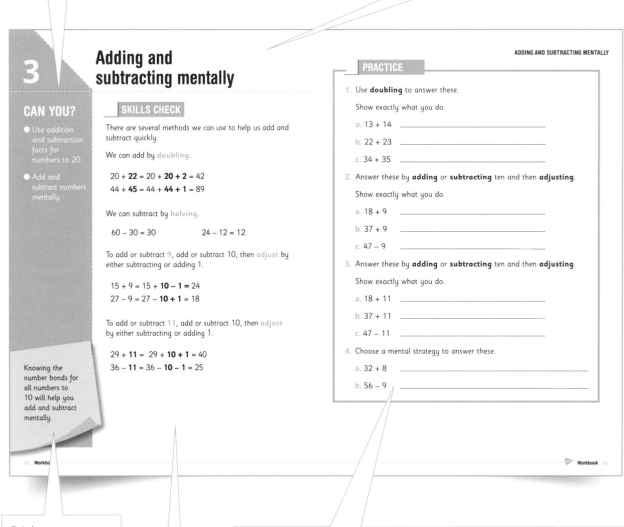

Sticky notes provide tips and reminders.

Complete the practice questions to check your understanding. The questions become more difficult as you go down the page.

Background information on the topic to help you answer the questions.

# Progress chart

| Topic | Skills checked | Practised | Aimed higher |
|---|---|---|---|
| Counting and representing number | | | |
| Place value, comparing and ordering numbers | | | |
| Adding and subtracting mentally | | | |
| Inverse operations | | | |
| Multiplying and dividing mentally | | | |
| Problem solving with multiplication and division | | | |
| Fractions | | | |
| Equivalent fractions | | | |
| Fractions of shapes | | | |
| Fractions of sets of objects | | | |
| Fractions of quantities | | | |
| Length | | | |
| Mass and temperature | | | |
| Capacity and volume | | | |
| Money | | | |
| Time | | | |
| 3D shapes | | | |
| 2D shapes | | | |
| Position, direction and turns | | | |
| Charts and tables | | | |

# Counting and representing number

- Count forwards and backwards in 2s, 3s and 5s from zero.

- Count forwards and backwards in 10s from any number.

- Identify and show numbers using different equipment.

Learn counting in 2s to 10 by heart: 2, 4, 6, 8, 10.

## SKILLS CHECK

These number lines show the numbers we say when counting in **2s, 3s and 5s** from zero to 50.

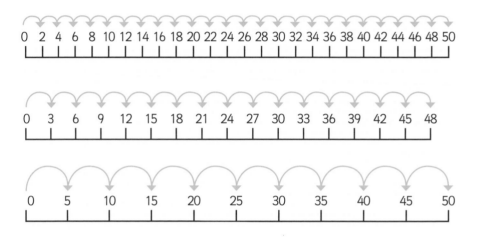

Count forwards, then backwards, along each number line.

When we count in **10s** from zero, the 1s digit always ends in a zero.

10, 20, 30, 40...

Count in 10s from 18.

Which digit appears in every number you say?

We can show numbers using equipment.

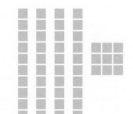

## PRACTICE

If you can count in 2s, you can also count in 20s and 200s.

1. Complete this count in **20s**.

   0, 20 _____ , _____ , _____ , _____ ,

   _____ , _____ , _____ , _____ ,

   _____ , _____ , _____ , 260

2. Complete this count in **200s**.

   1600, 1400 _____ , _____ , _____ ,

   _____ , _____ , _____ , 0

3. Write the **numbers** that are shown.

   a.
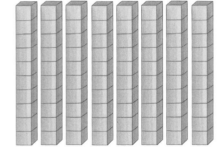

   b.

4. Draw a picture that shows **65** made from two different coloured counters.

5. a. Draw a picture to show **54**.

   b. Do it another way.

   c. And another.

# Place value, comparing and ordering numbers

## CAN YOU?

- Work out the value of each digit in a 2-digit number.

- Compare numbers using the symbols >, < and =.

- Order numbers from greatest to least, and from least to greatest.

## SKILLS CHECK

### Place value

| 10s | 1s |
|-----|----|
| 7   | 8  |

This grid shows **10s** and **1s**.

There are seven 10s and eight 1s.

We **multiply** the seven by ten to get its true value of 70:

$$7 \times 10 = \textbf{70}$$

We **multiply** the eight by one to get its true value of 8:

$$8 \times 1 = \textbf{8}$$

We **add** 70 and 8 to make the whole number of 78:

$$70 + 8 = \textbf{78}$$

### Comparing numbers

Look at these symbols.

> greater than

< less than

The small end of the **>** or **<** symbol points to the smaller number. The wider end points to the bigger number.

We can use them to compare two numbers and show which is the greatest and which is the least.

$$6 > 3 \qquad\qquad 3 < 6$$

### Ordering numbers

From **greatest** to **least**

73, 45, 29, 18, 12, 7

From **least** to **greatest**

7, 12, 18, 29, 45, 73

## PRACTICE

1. Write the **value** of each circled digit.

   a. 6⑧ _____

   b. ⑦4 _____

   c. ①4 _____

   d. 2⑦ _____

2. Explain why the digit **3** in 32 is 30.

   _____

   _____

3. Explain why the digit **7** in 17 is 7.

   _____

   _____

4. Compare these numbers.

   Write **>**, **<** or **=** in the spaces.

   a. 34 ____ 45 – 10

   b. 72 – 21 ____ 43

   c. 54 + 12 ____ 66

   d. 26 + 14 ____ 78 – 42

   e. 63 + 14 ____ 98 – 21

   f. 65 – 15 ____ 75 – 25

5. Order from **greatest** to **least**.

78, 87, 73, 37, 82, 28

_____

Explain how you know your order is correct.

_____

_____

_____

6. Answer these.

a. Smita is thinking of a number.
   Her number has **three 10s** and **eight 1s**.
   What is her number?

b. Luke is thinking of a number.
   His number is **two 10s greater** than Smita's number.
   What is his number?

c. Freddie is thinking of a number.
   His number is **five 1s less** than Luke's number.
   What is Freddie's number?

d. Order Smita's, Luke's and Freddie's number from **greatest** to **least**.

   greatest                least

   _____   _____   _____

# 3

# Adding and subtracting mentally

Knowing the number bonds for all numbers to 10 will help you add and subtract mentally.

## SKILLS CHECK

There are several methods we can use to help us add and subtract quickly.

We can add by **doubling**.

$$20 + \mathbf{22} = 20 + \mathbf{20 + 2} = 42$$
$$44 + \mathbf{45} = 44 + \mathbf{44 + 1} = 89$$

We can subtract by **halving**.

$$60 - 30 = 30 \qquad\qquad 24 - 12 = 12$$

To add or subtract **9**, add or subtract 10, then **adjust** by either subtracting or adding 1.

$$15 + 9 = 15 + \mathbf{10 - 1} = 24$$
$$27 - 9 = 27 - \mathbf{10 + 1} = 18$$

To add or subtract **11**, add or subtract 10, then **adjust** by either subtracting or adding 1.

$$29 + \mathbf{11} = 29 + \mathbf{10 + 1} = 40$$
$$36 - \mathbf{11} = 36 - \mathbf{10 - 1} = 25$$

## PRACTICE

1. Use **doubling** to answer these.

   Show exactly what you do.

   a. 13 + 14 _____

   b. 22 + 23 _____

   c. 34 + 35 _____

2. Answer these by **adding** or **subtracting** ten and then **adjusting**.

   Show exactly what you do.

   a. 18 + 9 _____

   b. 37 + 9 _____

   c. 47 – 9 _____

3. Answer these by **adding** or **subtracting** ten and then **adjusting**.

   Show exactly what you do.

   a. 18 + 11 _____

   b. 37 + 11 _____

   c. 47 – 11 _____

4. Choose a mental strategy to answer these.

   a. 32 + 8 _____

   b. 56 – 9 _____

5. Samir scored **37** points on a game.
Rob scored **9** points **less**.
How many points did **Rob** score?

Show how you worked this out.

_____

_____

6. How are adding and subtracting 9 and 11 the **same**?

They are the same because _____

_____

_____

How are they **different**?

They are different because _____

_____

_____

# 4

# Inverse operations

## CAN YOU?

- Show that numbers can be added in any order.

- Show that numbers cannot be subtracted in any order.

- Use the bar model to show that addition and subtraction are inverse.

## SKILLS CHECK

Addition is commutative.

This means the order in which we add two numbers does not matter – the answer will always be the same.

12 + 10 = 22          25 + 13 = 38

10 + 12 = 22          13 + 25 = 38

Subtraction is not commutative.

If we subtract two numbers in different orders we will not get the same answer.

36 – 12 = 24      but      12 – 36 **does not** equal 24

We call addition and subtraction inverse operations. One does the opposite of the other.

Look at this bar model.
It tells us four facts.

| 35 | |
|:---:|:---:|
| **20** | **15** |

35 – 20 = 15 and 35 – 15 = 20

20 + 15 = 35 and 15 + 20 = 35

## PRACTICE

1. Write the two **addition** and two **subtraction** facts that this bar model shows.

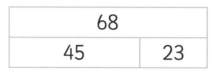

| 68 | |
|---|---|
| 45 | 23 |

Addition facts                           Subtraction facts

1. _____     1. _____

2. _____     2. _____

2. If you know that **34 + 56 = 90**, what other facts do you know?

_____

_____

_____

3. If you know that **78 – 56 = 22**, what other facts do you know?

_____

_____

_____

4. Work out the missing numbers.
   Write the numbers in the bar models.

a.  – 51 = 23          b. 67 – ⬚ = 42

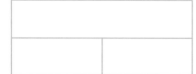

5. Draw a **bar model** to solve this problem.
   Joel had some marbles.
   He lost **19** during a game.
   He had **57** left.
   How many marbles did Joel have before losing some?

Joel had _____ marbles

6. Draw a **bar model** to solve this problem.
   Sophie had a collection of shells.
   She gave **36** to her friend.
   She had **42** left.
   How many shells did Sophie have before she gave some away?

Sophie had _____ shells

# Multiplying and dividing mentally

- Use multiplication and division facts for the 2, 5 and 10-times tables.

- Recognise odd and even numbers.

We only need to look at the ones digit of a number when deciding if it is odd or even.

## SKILLS CHECK

Being able to count in 2s, 5s and 10s is very useful for multiplying and dividing.

This is because the numbers we say when counting in these steps link to facts from the two, five and ten multiplication tables.

Using facts that we know to make other facts is another useful skill.

$$5 \times 2 = 10$$

From this fact we also know that $5 \times 20 = 100$ and $10 \times 20 = 200$.

An even number is a number that can be divided by two exactly without leaving a remainder.

Even numbers always end in 2, 4, 6, 8 or 0.

**32**, **106**, **84**, **400** and **1008** are **even** numbers

An odd number is an even number add 1.

Odd numbers always end in 1, 3, 5, 7 or 9.

**65**, **131**, **13**, **777**, and **1009** are **odd** numbers.

Do you think 560,490,007 is even or odd?

## PRACTICE

1.  Circle the **even** numbers.

    56    19    37    78    67    54    90    53    92    85    14

2.  When we count in **2s** from zero, do we say any odd numbers?

    _____

    Describe the pattern.

    _____

    _____

3.  Are there **odd** or **even** numbers when we count in **5s** from zero?

    _____

    Describe the pattern.

    _____

    _____

4.  Are there **odd** or **even** numbers when we count in **10s** from zero?

    _____

    Describe the pattern.

    _____

    _____

5. $7 \times 5 = 35$
   Write ten new facts from knowing this fact.

   1. _____

   2. _____

   3. _____

   4. _____

   5. _____

   6. _____

   7. _____

   8. _____

   9. _____

   10. _____

6. Jodie had **80** stamps.
   She stuck them equally among **five** books.
   How many stamps were there in each book?

   | stamps |

   Show how you worked out the answer.

   _____

   _____

# 6 Problem solving with multiplication and division

## CAN YOU?

● Show that numbers can be multiplied in any order.

● Show that numbers cannot be divided in any order.

● Use an array to show the relationship between multiplication and division.

If we know one multiplication fact we automatically know a second. If 4 × 3 = 12, then 3 × 4 = 12 too.

## SKILLS CHECK

Addition is commutative.

Multiplication is the same as repeated addition.

These three statements describe the same multiplication fact.

$$2 + 2 + 2 + 2 + 2 = 10$$
five lots of two = ten
$$2 \times 5 = 10$$

Like addition, multiplication is commutative.

Division is the same as repeated subtraction.

$$8 - 2 - 2 - 2 - 2 = 0 \quad \text{is the same as} \quad 8 \div 2 = 4$$

Division is not commutative.

10 ÷ 5 equals 2 but 5 ÷ 10 does not equal 2.

From an array, we can discover two multiplication facts and two division facts.

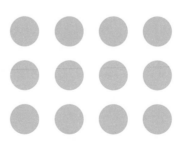

$$4 \times 3 = 12 \text{ and } 3 \times 4 = 12$$
$$12 \div 4 = 3 \text{ and } 12 \div 3 = 4$$

## PRACTICE

1. Write these as **repeated addition** statements.

   a. $7 \times 2$ _____

   b. $8 \times 7$ _____

2. Write the **four** facts that this array shows.

   1. _____

   2. _____

   3. _____

   4. _____

3. Mark these calculations. Use a tick (✓) or a cross (✗).

   $8 \times 5 = 4 \times 10$ ☐          $50 \div 5 = 5 \div 10$ ☐

   $16 \div 2 = 2 \div 16$ ☐          $12 \times 2 = 8 \times 3$ ☐

4. Draw an **array** to solve this problem.
   Ellie had **24** apples.
   She put them into containers.
   She put **four** apples into each one.
   How many containers did she use?

   Ellie used _____ containers

# 7 Fractions

## CAN YOU?

● Show $\frac{1}{2}$, $\frac{1}{4}$ and $\frac{1}{3}$ in different ways.

● Describe halves as parts of a whole.

● Describe quarters as parts of a whole.

The **denominator** (bottom number) of a fraction tells you how many parts the shape has been divided into.

### SKILLS CHECK

Fractions are parts of one or more wholes.

The parts are always equal areas.

These diagrams show halves of one whole.

The parts look different but they take up the same amount of space. The parts have the same area.

To find one half of anything, share the whole into two equal parts.

To find one third of anything, share the whole into three equal parts.

To find one quarter of anything, share the whole into four equal parts.

## PRACTICE

1. My whole is a group of flags.

   a. How many **parts** are there? \_\_\_\_

   b. What fraction have **stars**?
      Write your answer in two different ways.

1. [ __ ]   2. [ __ ]

   c. What fraction have **stripes**?
      Write your answer in two different ways.

1. [ __ ]   2. [ __ ]

   d. What do your answers to parts **b** and **c** tell you?

_____

2. a. Look at this rectangle and divide it into **two** equal parts.

   b. What fraction is each part?

[ __ ]

   c. If the whole is £12, what are the parts?  £ [ ] and £ [ ]

   d. If the whole is £24, what are the parts?  £ [ ] and £ [ ]

3. a. Look at this rectangle and divide it into **three** equal parts.

   b. What fraction is each part?

   $\dfrac{\phantom{0}}{\phantom{0}}$

   c. If the whole is £12, what are the parts?

   £ _____ , £ _____ and £ _____

   d. If the whole is £24, what are the parts?

   £ _____ and £ _____

4. a. Look at this rectangle and divide it into **four** equal parts.

   b. What fraction is each part?

   $\dfrac{\phantom{0}}{\phantom{0}}$

   c. If the whole is £12, what are the parts?

   £ _____ , £ _____ , £ _____ and £ _____

# 8 Equivalent fractions

## CAN YOU?

● Explain what one half is.

● Explain what one quarter is.

● Say what the word equivalent means.

● Know $\frac{1}{2} = \frac{2}{4}$

When the top and bottom number in a fraction are the same, the fraction is equal to one whole.

**SKILLS CHECK**

We can use the bar model to describe fractions.

| $\frac{1}{2}$ | $\frac{1}{2}$ |
|---|---|

**Two** halves make a **whole**.

| $\frac{1}{4}$ | $\frac{1}{4}$ | $\frac{1}{4}$ | $\frac{1}{4}$ |
|---|---|---|---|

**Four** quarters make a **whole**.

If we place the two fraction bars one on top of the other, we can see a link between halves and quarters.

| $\frac{1}{2}$ | $\frac{1}{2}$ |
|---|---|
| $\frac{1}{4}$ $\frac{1}{4}$ | $\frac{1}{4}$ $\frac{1}{4}$ |

**Two quarters** take up the same space as **one half.**

Two quarters are equivalent to one half.

What other links can you see?

## PRACTICE

1. Look at these fraction bars.

| 1 whole | | | | | | | |
|---|---|---|---|---|---|---|---|
| $\frac{1}{2}$ | | | | $\frac{1}{2}$ | | | |
| $\frac{1}{3}$ | | $\frac{1}{3}$ | | | $\frac{1}{3}$ | | |
| $\frac{1}{4}$ | | $\frac{1}{4}$ | | $\frac{1}{4}$ | | $\frac{1}{4}$ | |

   a. Write down all the other **equivalences** that you can see.

   b. Order the **fractions** in the fraction bars from **greatest** to **least**.

   **greatest**                    **least**

2. Iris says that $\frac{1}{4}$ is bigger than $\frac{1}{2}$ because 4 is bigger than 2.

   Explain why this is incorrect. Use a drawing to help you explain. Then draw another.

# Fractions of shapes

**SKILLS CHECK**

We can show different fractions of shapes.

The fractions must have equal areas.

Sometimes the areas are the same shape but they don't have to be.

**Half** is shaded.

One **quarter** is shaded.

One **third** is shaded.

Can you say what fraction of this shape is shaded?

## PRACTICE

1. Shade a **quarter** of this shape.
   Think carefully about how you can divide it into **four** equal parts.

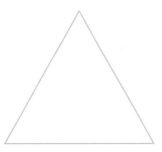

2. Look at this shape.

   a. What fraction is shaded?

   b. There is an equivalent fraction that we can write for part a. What is it?

3. This shape has been divided into **quarters**.
   Make a copy of it and prove that each piece is a quarter.
   You can cut or fold the pieces.

   Explain how you know that each piece is a quarter.

   _____

   _____

   _____

   _____

# 10 Fractions of sets of objects

## CAN YOU?

- Find half of a set of objects.

- Find a third of a set of objects.

- Find a quarter of a set of objects.

- Find three quarters of a set of objects.

Remember, finding a half is the same as dividing by 2.

## SKILLS CHECK

We can show different fractions of sets of objects.

**Four** out of **eight** leaves are shaded.

That is $\frac{1}{2}$.

**One** bird out of **three** is shaded.

That is $\frac{1}{3}$.

**One** feather out of **four** is shaded.

That is $\frac{1}{4}$.

What fraction of the feathers is unshaded?

**PRACTICE**

1. Here are eight stars.

   a. Shade $\frac{1}{4}$ of the stars.

   b. How many stars have you shaded? ☐

2. Here are eight buttons.

   a. Shade $\frac{3}{4}$ of the buttons.

   b. How many buttons have you shaded? ☐

3. Here are nine cakes.

   a. Shade $\frac{1}{3}$ of the cakes.

   b. How many cakes have you shaded? ☐

4. Here are another nine cakes.

   a. Shade $\frac{2}{3}$ of the cakes.

   b. How many cakes have you shaded? ☐

# Fractions of quantities

## SKILLS CHECK

We can find fractions of quantities using the bar model.

| 8 | |
|---|---|
| 4 | 4 |

The whole is eight.

Eight is shared into **two** equal parts, or **halves**.

Each part is four.    $\frac{1}{2}$ of 8 = 4

| 8 | | | |
|---|---|---|---|
| 2 | 2 | 2 | 2 |

The whole is eight.

Eight is shared into **four** equal parts, or **quarters**.

Each part is two.    $\frac{1}{4}$ of 8 = 2

| 12 | | |
|---|---|---|
| 4 | 4 | 4 |

The whole is 12.

12 is shared into **three** equal parts, or **thirds**.

Each part is four.    $\frac{1}{3}$ of 12 = 4

## PRACTICE

1. $\frac{1}{2}$ of the sweets in a tin are chocolates.

   $\frac{1}{4}$ are toffees.

   The rest are mints.

   There are 6 mints.

   How many sweets are in the tin?

   Write your answer in the bar model.

   | _____ sweets are in the tin | | |
   | --- | --- | --- |
   | chocolates | toffees | 6 mints |

2. Use the bar model in question **1** to find out how many sweets are in the tin if it contains these quantities of mints.

   a. 15 [ ]

   b. 21 [ ]

   c. 25 [ ]

   d. 30 [ ]

   e. 42 [ ]

3. Complete the bar model to show this problem.

   $\frac{1}{4}$ of the children on a coach are boys.

   The rest are girls.

   There are 60 girls.

   How many children are on the coach?

   | _____ children on the coach | | | |
   | --- | --- | --- | --- |
   | | | | |

# 12 Length

## CAN YOU?

● Measure length and height in metres and centimetres.

● Order lengths from shortest to longest, and from longest to shortest.

● Compare lengths using the symbols >, < and =.

## SKILLS CHECK

We measure length using metres and centimetres. When recording the length of an object we write m for metres and cm for centimetres.

Small objects are measured in centimetres, such as the length of a pen or the length of a book.

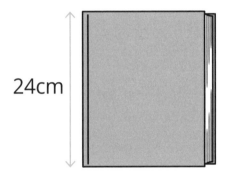

24cm

Larger objects are measured in metres. Examples are the height of a door frame or the length of a room.

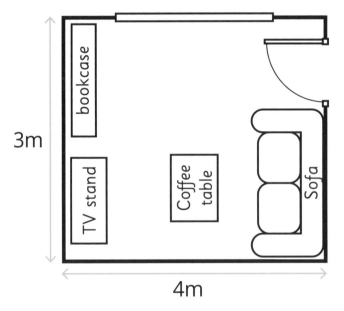

3m

4m

There are 100cm in 1m.

From this fact we can work out other facts.

$$50cm = \tfrac{1}{2}metre \qquad 200cm = 2m$$

## PRACTICE

1. 600cm = 6m        2000m = 20m

   Use these equivalences to come up with 10 more facts.

   Be creative!

   1._____

   2._____

   3._____

   4._____

   5._____

   6._____

   7._____

   8._____

   9._____

   10._____

2. Draw lines of these lengths:

   a. 5cm

   b. 8cm

   c. $12\frac{1}{2}$cm

3. Measure these lines. Write the measurements in the boxes.

   a. _____

| | |
|---|---|
| | cm |

   b. _____

| | |
|---|---|
| | cm |

   c. Compare the lengths of the lines in parts **a** and **b**.
      Write the lengths either side of the > and < symbols.

     _____ > _____

     _____ < _____

   d. Complete the number statement.
      Show what needs to be added to the shortest length
      to make the two lengths equal.

     _____ + _____ = _____

   e. Complete the number statement.
      Show what needs to be subtracted from the longest length
      to make the two lengths equal.

     _____ − _____ = _____

   f. What do you notice from your answers to parts **d** and **e**?

     _____

     _____

# 13 Mass and temperature

## CAN YOU?

● Measure mass in kilograms and grams.

● Compare masses using the symbols >, < and =.

● Order temperatures from hottest to coolest, and coolest to hottest.

0°C is very cold. It is when water turns to ice!

## SKILLS CHECK

### Mass

We measure **mass** using **kilograms** and **grams**. When recording the mass of an object we write **kg** for kilograms and **g** for grams.

There are 1000g in 1kg.

From this fact we can work out other facts.

$$2000g = 2kg \qquad 7000g = 7kg$$

We use scales to measure mass.

**2kg**

### Temperature

We measure **temperature** using a **thermometer**. We record temperature in **Celsius**, like this: °C.

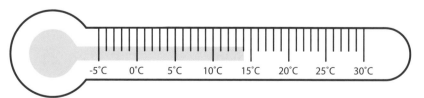

These temperatures are ordered from coolest to warmest.

$$2°C, 5°C, 14°C, 19°C$$

## PRACTICE

1. **3000g = 3kg**

   Use this fact to write five other gram/kilogram **equivalences**.

   1. _____

   2. _____

   3. _____

   4. _____

   5. _____

2. Write the masses.

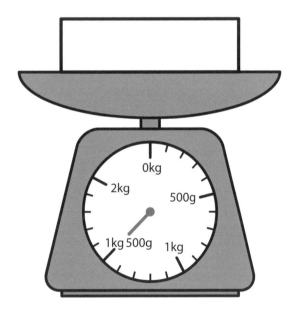 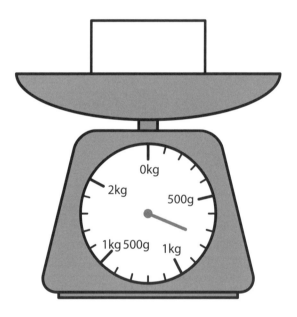

   _____     _____

3. Compare the masses. Write **>** or **<** between each pair.

   a. 1kg 500g ____ 750g          b. 1kg 250g ____ 2kg 800g

   c. 750g ____ 2kg 800g          d. 1kg 600g ____ 1650g

4. What must you add to 750g to make it equal to 1kg 500g?

   750g + _____ = 1kg 500g

5. What must you subtract from 1kg 500g to make it equal to 750g?

   1kg 500g – _____ = 750g

6. What do you notice about your answers to questions **5** and **6**?

   _____

   _____

7. Write these masses in **grams**.

   a. 1kg 500g _____

   b. 2kg 800g _____

8. Write these masses in **kilograms** and **grams**.

   a. 2500g _____

   b. 1600g _____

9. Look at these temperatures.

   23°C    10°C    27°C    31°C    5°C

   a. Order from **coolest** to **warmest**.

      **greatest**                                              **least**

      _____  _____  _____  _____  _____

   b. What is the **difference** between the coolest
      and the warmest temperatures?                    [        ] °C

# 14

# Capacity and volume

## CAN YOU?

- Measure capacity in litres and millilitres.

- Order capacities from greatest to least, and least to greatest.

- Compare capacities using the symbols for >, < and =.

## SKILLS CHECK

We measure capacity and volume using litres and millilitres. When recording the capacity or volume of a container, we write l for litres and ml for millilitres.

We use millilitres to measure the amount held in small containers, such as a cup. We use litres to measure the amount held in larger containers, such as a swimming pool.

There are 1000ml in 1l.

Capacity is the amount a container will hold.
Volume is the amount inside a container.

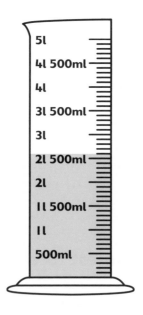

The capacity is 5l
The volume is 2l 600ml

## PRACTICE

1. Order the volumes from **least** to **greatest**.

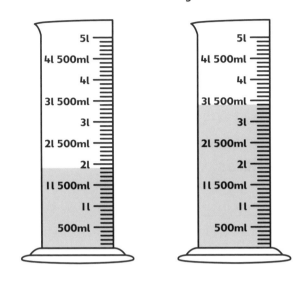
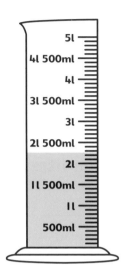
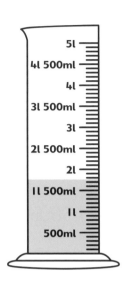

least                                                                              greatest

_____   _____   _____   _____   _____

2. Compare these volumes.
   Write **>** or **<** between each pair.

   a. 1l 300ml _____ 1l 750ml

   b. 500ml _____ 2l 500ml

   c. 2l 750ml _____ 2l 250ml

3. What must you add to 250ml to make it equal to 1l?

   250ml + _____ = 1l

4. What must you subtract from 1l to make it equal to 250ml?

   1l – _____ = 250ml

5. What do you notice about your answers to questions **3** and **4**?

   _____

   _____

6. Write these volumes in **millilitres**.

    a. 1l 300ml _____

    b. 2l 500ml _____

    c. 3l 250ml _____

7. Write these volumes in **litres** and **millilitres**.

    a. 4500ml _____

    b. 2900ml _____

    c. 1750ml _____

8. Suzie has a water bottle that has a capacity of 500ml.
   Jonnie has one that holds three times as much.
   Find the **total capacity** of the two bottles.
   Draw a **bar model** to show your working.

Total capacity _____

# 15 Money

## CAN YOU?

- Know the symbols for pounds (£) and pence (p).

- Use different combinations of coins to make the same amount of money.

- Combine coins to make a particular value.

- Solve money problems that involve adding and subtracting and giving change.

Remember there are 100p in £1.

## SKILLS CHECK

In the United Kingdom, money is in **pounds** and **pence**. Pounds are written as **£** and pence are written as **p**.

These are the coins we use in the United Kingdom.

We can group different coins together to make the same amount.

These groups of coins total 33p.

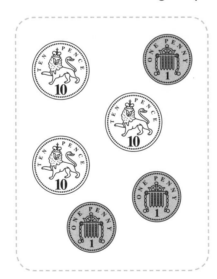 

Imagine you buy a pencil for 44p. You give the shopkeeper one 50p coin. What change will you be given?

$$50p - 44p = 6p$$

## PRACTICE

1. List all the ways you can make **20p** using five coins or fewer.

   _____

   _____

2. Look at these purses.

   a. How much money is in the first purse? _____

   b. How much money is in the second purse? _____

   c. What is the **difference** between the two amounts of money?

   _____

3. Compare these amounts of money.
   Write **>** or **<** between each pair.

   a. £1.25 _____ £1.35       b. 98p _____ 64p       c. £3.50 _____ £2.75

4. What must you **add** to £1.25 to make it equal to £1.35?

   £1.25 + _____ = £1.35

5. What must you **subtract** from £1.35 to make it equal to £1.25?

   £1.25 = £1.35 − _____

6. What do you notice from your answers to questions **5** and **6**?

   _____

   _____

7. Write these amounts in **pence**.

   a. £1.20 _____

   b. £1.75 _____

8. Write these amounts in **pounds and pence**.

   a. 145p _____

   b. 290p _____

9. Fahmida spent $\frac{1}{4}$ of her money on a book.
   The book cost £5. How much money did she have to begin with?

   a. Draw a **bar model** to show the problem.




   Fahmida had _____

   b. What if the book cost £8? _____

10. Hamish spent $\frac{1}{3}$ of his money on some toy cars.
    The cars cost £10. How much money did he have to begin with?

   a. Draw a **bar model** to show this problem.




   Hamish had _____

   b. What if the cars cost £20? _____

# 16 Time

## CAN YOU?

● Tell and write the time to the nearest five minutes.

● Say the number of minutes in an hour.

● Say the number of hours in a day.

● Compare and order different periods of time.

When reading times to the hour, look at the number that the hour hand will get to next.

## SKILLS CHECK

We use clocks and watches to tell the time.

There are five minutes when the long hand moves from one hour number to the next.

This clock shows quarter past ten.
15 minutes have passed since 10 o'clock.
You can check this by counting in 5s
from 12 to 3 round the clock face.

There are 60 minutes in one hour.

By doubling, we know that there must be 120 minutes in two hours.

There are 24 hours in one day.

By doubling, we know that there must be 48 hours in two days.

A football match lasts for 90 minutes.
A netball match lasts for 60 minutes.
A rugby match lasts for 80 minutes.

| **longest** | | **shortest** |
|---|---|---|
| football | rugby | netball |

## PRACTICE

1. Write the number of **minutes** there are in:

   a. four hours _____

   b. eight hours _____

2. There are seven days in a week.
   Write the number of **days** in:

   a. four weeks _____

   b. eight weeks _____

3. Tell the time.

   a.  _____

   b.  _____

   c. _____

4. Kayo went for a bike ride. She set off from home at 10 o'clock. She was out for one and a half hours.

   a. What time did she get home?

   _____

   b. What if she set off at half past ten?

   _____

   c. What if she set off at quarter past 11?

   _____

   d. What if she set off at quarter to 12?

   _____

5. Sally started her homework at 4 o'clock and finished at quarter to 5.

   a. How long did she spend on her homework?

   _____

   b. What if she finished at quarter past 5?

   _____

   c. What if she finished at 10 minutes to 5?

   _____

   d. What if she finished at 5 minutes past 5?

   _____

# 3D shapes

## SKILLS CHECK

There are many different types of 3D shapes. Some have curved surfaces and some have all flat faces.

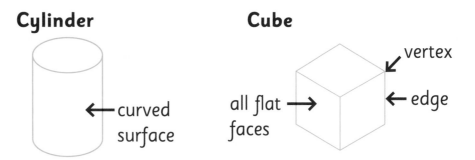

**Cylinder** — curved surface

**Cube** — vertex, all flat faces, edge

3D shapes such as the cube above have faces, edges and vertices.

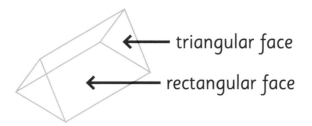

triangular face

rectangular face

Prisms have ends that are the same shape and all the other faces are rectangular.

A pyramid is a shape where the base is a polygon (straight-sided flat shape) and the sides are triangles which meet at the top.

Some 2D shapes make the faces of 3D shapes. The faces of this pyramid are 4 triangles.

A vertex is like a corner. The plural is vertices.

## PRACTICE

1. Tick the **pyramids**.

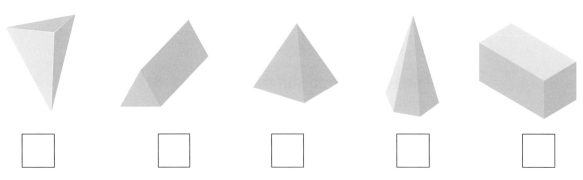

☐       ☐       ☐       ☐       ☐

2. Tick the **prisms**.

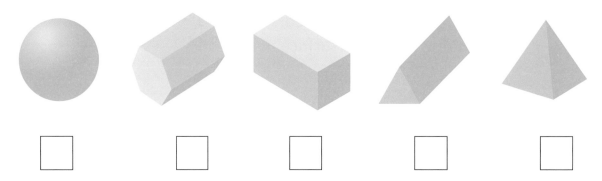

☐       ☐       ☐       ☐       ☐

3. A 3D shape has **five faces**. One face is **square**. What shape is it?

_____

4. A 3D shape is a **prism**. All the faces are **square**. What shape is it?

_____

5. A 3D shape has one curved surface. It has one flat face which is a **circle**. What shape is it?

_____

# 18 2D shapes

## CAN YOU?

● Identify 2D shapes.

● Describe the features of 2D shapes.

● Identify symmetry in 2D shapes.

### SKILLS CHECK

**2D shapes** can be regular or irregular.

**Regular** shapes have sides that are the same length and corners that are the same size.

**Irregular** shapes do not have sides that are the same length. The corners are not the same size.

Regular pentagon            Irregular pentagon

We can identify 2D shapes by the number of sides and corners they have.

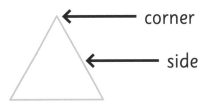

corner

side

3 sides        3 corners

A quadrilateral is any four-sided 2D shape. A regular quadrilateral is a square.

A 2D shape is **symmetrical** if one half of it is identical to the other.

A rectangle is **symmetrical**.

## PRACTICE

1. Draw three different triangles.

2. Draw three different **quadrilaterals**.

3. Use a ruler to draw all the **lines of symmetry** on this equilateral triangle.

   How many lines of symmetry have you drawn?

4. Use a ruler to draw all the **lines of symmetry** on this square.

   How many lines of symmetry have you drawn?

# 19

## Position, direction and turns

# CAN YOU?

- Describe position, direction and movement using mathematical vocabulary.

- Identify the relationship between quarter, half and three-quarter turns and right angles.

### SKILLS CHECK

### Position and direction

There are lots of words we can use to describe position and direction.

| Position | Direction |
|---|---|
| We can put a chair under a table. | We can swim forwards. |
| A goat can jump over a gate. | A crab walks sideways. |
| Julie is wearing her coat on top of her jumper. | A car turns left at the traffic lights. |

### Turns

When we turn, we move to the right or the left. We can make a quarter turn, a half turn, a three-quarter turn and a whole turn.

Make a quarter turn to the left or the right. This turn is sometimes called a right angle.

Make a half turn to the left. Where is the object you were originally facing?

Make a whole turn. What do you notice?

A turn to the right is described as **clockwise**.
A turn to the left is described as **anticlockwise**.

## PRACTICE

1. Write a sentence to describe the **position** of the circle in relation to the two triangles.

_____

2. Write a sentence to describe the **position** of the triangles in relation to the circle.

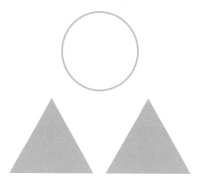

_____

3. How many quarter turns make a whole turn? _____

4. Tick the arrows that show a **quarter** turn.

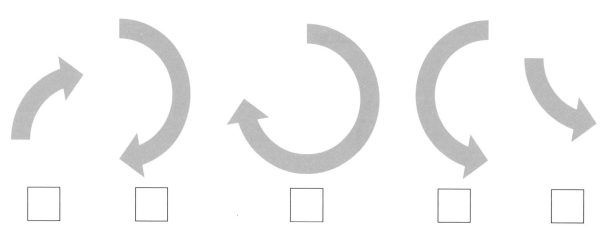

5. Fill in the gap to complete the statement.

Half a turn + _____ is a three-quarter turn.

6. This arrow shows a turn in a **clockwise** direction.

Why do you think it is called a clockwise direction?

_____

7. This arrow shows a turn in an **anticlockwise** direction.

Why do you think it is called an anticlockwise direction?

_____

8. This line shows the route through a maze.
Describe the route the man must take to reach the finish.

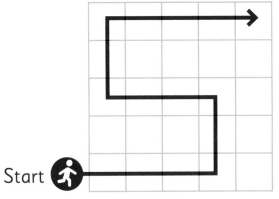

_____

_____

# 20

# Charts and tables

## CAN YOU?

- Understand tables and tally charts.

- Show information on a pictogram or block diagram.

- Ask and answer questions using a pictogram or block diagram.

## SKILLS CHECK

### Tally charts

The children in Year 2 were asked to name their favourite fruit. The children's responses were recorded using tallies. Tallies are a quick way of keeping count during a survey. They are counted in fives.

This chart displays the survey results as tally marks and totals.

| Fruit | Tally | Total |
|-------|-------|-------|
| Apple | ‖‖‖ ‖‖‖ ‖‖‖ | 13 |
| Banana | ‖‖‖ ‖‖‖ | 10 |
| Grapes | ‖‖‖ ‖‖‖ ‖‖‖ ‖‖ | 17 |
| Kiwi | ‖‖‖ ‖‖ | 7 |
| Pineapple | ‖‖‖ | 3 |

### Pictograms

A pictogram is a chart that uses symbols to show information. Here is the information about Year 2's favourite fruit presented as a pictogram.

| Fruit | Number of children who chose it |
|-------|--------------------------------|
| Apple | ●●●●●●●●●●●●● |
| Banana | ●●●●●●●●●● |
| Grapes | ●●●●●●●●●●●●●●●●● |
| Kiwi | ●●●●●●● |
| Pineapple | ●●● |

● = one child

**Block diagrams** present information in columns. Here is the information about Year 2's favourite fruit presented as a block diagram.

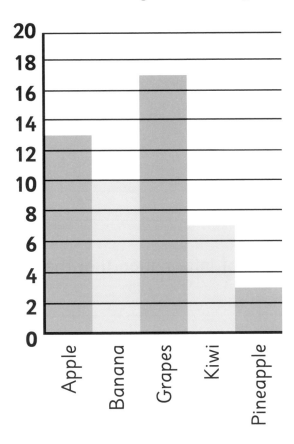

**Favourite fruit survey**

From the tally chart, pictogram and block diagram showing Year 2's favourite fruit, we can learn facts such as:

How many children voted.

Which is the most popular fruit.

Which is the least popular fruit.

How many children prefer apples to kiwis.

How many like grapes.

## PRACTICE

1. Look at this table.

   a. Draw the **tally marks** in the empty column.

   | Favourite pet | Tally | Number of children |
   |---|---|---|
   | Dog | | 12 |
   | Cat | | 9 |
   | Rabbit | | 7 |
   | Hamster | | 6 |
   | Guinea pig | | 8 |

   b. Write **three** pieces of information that the table tells you.

   _____

   _____

   _____

   c. Fill in this **pictogram** to show the information from the tally. Each symbol should represent two children.

   | Favourite pet | Number of children |
   |---|---|
   | Dog | |
   | Cat | |
   | Rabbit | |
   | Hamster | |
   | Guinea pig | |

   d. How many children were asked about their favourite pets? [ ]

2. This **block diagram** shows some children's favourite sports.

### Children's favourite sports

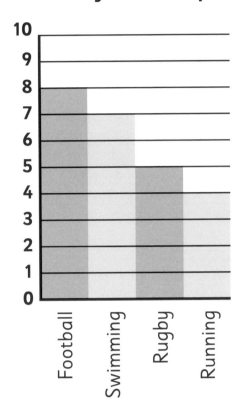

a. How many children voted for football and running?

b. How many more children voted for swimming than rugby?

c. How many children were asked about their favourite sport?

d. Write **three** questions that you could ask your friend to answer from this block diagram.

_____

_____

_____

# Answers

The answers are given below. They are referenced by page number and question number. The answers usually only include the information the children are expected to give. There may be some places where the answers vary or multiple answers are acceptable, these are marked as such. Note that in some places, answers will be varied and subjective from child to child, and a fair degree of marker discretion and interpretation is needed, particularly if children's understanding and skills have to be deduced from their answers.

| Page | Q | Answers |
|---|---|---|
| 7 | 1 | 0, 20, **40**, **60**, **80**, **100**, **120**, **140**, **160**, **180**, **200**, **220**, **240**, 260 |
| | 2 | 1600, 1400, **1200**, **1000**, **800**, **600**, **400**, **200**, 0 |
| | 3 | **a.** 85 **b.** 75 |
| 8 | 4 | Children's choices. Expect children to be able to explain how they have shown 65. |
| | 5 | Children's choices. Expect children to be able to explain how they have shown 54 in three different ways. |
| 10 | 1 | **a.** 8 ones: 8 **b.** 7 tens: 70 **c.** 1 ten: 10 **d.** 7 ones: 7 |
| | 2 | For example: 3 is in the 10s position so must be multiplied by ten to give its true value of 30. |
| | 3 | For example: 7 is in the 1s position so must be multiplied by one to give its true value of 7. |
| | 4 | **a.** < **b.** > **c.** = **d.** > **e.** = **f.** = |
| 11 | 5 | 87, 82, 78, 73, 37, 28<br>Accept explanations that show children understand that they look at the 10s digits first. If some of the 10s digits are the same, they then look at the 1s digits. The higher the 10s digit, the greater the number. |
| | 6 | **a.** 38 **b.** 58 **c.** 53 **d.** 58, 53, 38 |
| 13 | 1 | **a.** 13 + 13 + 1 = 27 or 14 + 14 − 1 = 27<br>**b.** 22 + 22 + 1 = 45 or 23 + 23 − 1 = 45<br>**c.** 34 + 34 + 1 = 69 or 35 + 35 − 1 = 69 |
| | 2 | **a.** 18 + 10 − 1 = 27<br>**b.** 37 + 10 − 1 = 46<br>**c.** 47 − 10 + 1 = 38 |
| | 3 | **a.** 18 + 10 + 1 = 29<br>**b.** 37 + 10 + 1 = 48<br>**c.** 47 − 10 − 1 = 36 |
| | 4 | **a.** 40 **b.** 47 |
| 14 | 5 | 28    37 − 10 + 1 |
| | 6 | Accept explanations that show understanding. For example: They are the same because both involve adding or subtracting ten. They are different because when adding nine you subtract one; when adding 11 you add one. When subtracting nine you add one; when subtracting 11 you subtract one. |
| 16 | 1 | 45 + 23 = 68, 23 + 45 = 68; 68 − 45 = 23, 68 − 23 = 45 |
| | 2 | 56 + 34 = 90, 90 − 56 = 34, 90 − 34 = 56 |
| | 3 | 78 − 22 = 56, 22 + 56 = 78, 56 + 22 = 78 |
| | 4 | **a.**<br>| 74 |<br>| 51 | 23 |<br>**b.**<br>| 67 |<br>| 42 | 25 |<br>NB the bottom two numbers in each bar can be in either order. |
| 17 | 5 | | 76 |<br>| 19 | 57 |<br>Joel had 76 marbles. |
| | 6 | | 78 |<br>| 36 | 42 |<br>Sophie had 78 shells. |

| Page | Q | Answers |
|------|---|---------|
| **19** | 1 | 56   78   54   90   92   14 |
| | 2 | No. Accept explanations that show that children understand the pattern. For example: the pattern will be 0, 2, 4, 6, 8; numbers either side of an odd number are even. |
| | 3 | Yes, there are both odd and even numbers. Accept explanations that show that children understand the pattern is odd, even, odd, even. |
| | 4 | Even numbers. Accept explanations that show that children understand the pattern is always even because the 1s digits always end in zero. |
| **20** | 5 | Answers will vary and may include: $5 \times 7 = 35$; $35 \div 5 = 7$; $35 \div 7 = 5$; $50 \times 7 = 350$; $5 \times 70 = 350$; $350 \div 50 = 7$; $350 \div 70 = 5$; $500 \times 7 = 3500$; $5 \times 700 = 3500$; $3500 \div 500 = 7$; $3500 \div 700 = 5$ |
| | 6 | 16 |
| **22** | 1 | **a.** $7 + 7$ <br> **b.** $8 + 8 + 8 + 8 + 8 + 8 + 8$ |
| | 2 | $6 \times 3 = 18$, $3 \times 6 = 18$, $18 \div 3 = 6$, $18 \div 6 = 3$ |
| | 3 | $8 \times 5 = 4 \times 10$ ✓ <br> $50 \div 5 = 5 \div 10$ ✗ <br> $16 \div 2 = 2 \div 16$ ✗ <br> $12 \times 2 = 8 \times 3$ ✓ |
| | 4 | <br> Ellie used six containers. |
| **24** | 1 | **a.** 4   **b.** $\frac{1}{2}$, $\frac{2}{4}$   **c.** $\frac{1}{2}$, $\frac{2}{4}$   **d.** $\frac{1}{2} = \frac{2}{4}$ |
| | 2 | **a.** There are several different options. Accept any answer that shows the rectangle divided into two equal parts. <br> **b.** $\frac{1}{2}$   **c.** £6   **d.** £12 |
| **25** | 3 | **a.** There are two obvious options. Accept any answer that shows the rectangle divided into three equal parts. <br> **b.** $\frac{1}{3}$   **c.** £4   **d.** £8 |
| | 4 | **a.** There are several different options. Accept any answer that shows the rectangle divided into four equal parts. <br> **b.** $\frac{1}{4}$   **c.** £3 |
| **27** | 1 | **a.** There are several equivalent fractions. <br> $\frac{2}{2} = 1$, $\frac{3}{3} = 1$, $\frac{4}{4} = 1$ <br> **b.** $\frac{1}{2}$, $\frac{1}{3}$, $\frac{1}{4}$ |
| | 2 | Iris is incorrect. Accept explanations in words or drawings that show children understand that $\frac{1}{4}$ is the whole divided into 4 equal parts and $\frac{1}{2}$ is the whole divided into two equal parts therefore $\frac{1}{4}$ is smaller than $\frac{1}{2}$. |
| **29** | 1 | |
| | 2 | **a.** $\frac{1}{2}$   **b.** $\frac{2}{4}$   or   **a.** $\frac{2}{4}$   **b.** $\frac{1}{2}$ |
| | 3 | Children should be able to prove that each piece is the same fraction by cutting out the triangles and halving them by cutting or folding. <br> Children's explanations will vary but expect them to describe their method for establishing that each piece is a quarter. |

# ANSWERS

| Page | Q | Answers |
|---|---|---|
| 31 | 1 | **a.** Any two stars shaded   **b.** 2 |
| | 2 | **a.** Any six buttons shaded   **b.** 6 |
| | 3 | **a.** Any three cakes shaded   **b.** 3 |
| | 4 | **a.** Any six cakes shaded   **b.** 6 |
| 33 | 1 | <table><tr><td colspan="3">24 sweets are in the tin</td></tr><tr><td>chocolates</td><td>toffees</td><td>6 mints</td></tr></table> |
| | 2 | **a.** 60   **b.** 84   **c.** 100   **d.** 120   **e.** 168 |
| | 3 | <table><tr><td colspan="4">80 children on the coach</td></tr><tr><td>$\frac{1}{4}$ or 20 (boys)</td><td>20 (girls)</td><td>20 (girls)</td><td>20 (girls)</td></tr></table> |
| 35 | 1 | There are many possible answers. For example: 6000cm = 60m; 60,000cm = 600m; 300cm = 3m; 150cm = $1\frac{1}{2}$m; 1200cm = 12m; 2m = 200cm; 1m = 100cm; 4m = 400cm; 40m = 4000cm; 50cm = $\frac{1}{2}$m |
| | 2 | **a.** Check for accurate drawing of a line measuring 5cm<br>**b.** Check for accurate drawing of a line measuring 8cm<br>**c.** Check for accurate drawing of a line measuring $12\frac{1}{2}$cm |
| 36 | 3 | **a.** $7\frac{1}{2}$cm<br>**b.** 13cm<br>**c.** 13cm > $7\frac{1}{2}$ cm   $7\frac{1}{2}$ cm < 13cm<br>**d.** $7\frac{1}{2}$ cm + $5\frac{1}{2}$ cm = 13cm<br>**e.** 13cm − $5\frac{1}{2}$ cm = $7\frac{1}{2}$ cm<br>**f.** The same length needs adding or subtracting to make the lengths equal. |
| 38 | 1 | There are many possible answers. For example: 1500g = $1\frac{1}{2}$kg; 30,000g = 30kg; 6000g = 6kg; 9000 = 9kg; 12,000g = 12kg |
| | 2 | 1kg 500g, 750g |
| | 3 | **a.** >   **b.** <   **c.** <   **d.** < |
| 39 | 4 | 750g |
| | 5 | 750g |
| | 6 | The same amount is added or subtracted to make the two masses equal. |
| | 7 | **a.** 1500g   **b.** 2800g |
| | 8 | **a.** 2kg 500g   **b.** 1kg 600g |
| | 9 | **a.** 5°C, 10°C, 23°C, 27°C, 31°C   **b.** 26°C |
| 41 | 1 | 1l 750ml, 1l 900ml, 2l 250ml, 3l 400ml |
| | 2 | **a.** <   **b.** <   **c.** > |
| | 3 | 750ml |
| | 4 | 750ml |
| | 5 | The same amount is added or subtracted to make the two measurements equal. |
| 42 | 6 | **a** 1300ml   **b.** 2500ml   **c.** 3250ml |
| | 7 | **a.** 4l 500ml   **b.** 2l 900ml   **c.** 1l 750ml |
| | 8 | Example of bar model is shown below, total capacity is 2000ml or 2l<br><table><tr><td>500ml</td><td>500ml</td><td>500ml</td><td>500ml</td></tr><tr><td colspan="4">2000ml or 2l</td></tr></table> |

| Page | Q | Answers |
|---|---|---|
| **44** | 1 | 20p    10p + 10p    10p + 5p + 5p    5p + 5p + 5p + 5p    10p + 5p + 2p + 2p + 1p |
| | 2 | **a.** £1.21    **b.** £1.14    **c.** 7p |
| | 3 | **a.** <    **b.** >    **c.** > |
| | 4 | 10p or £.010 |
| | 5 | 10p or £0.10 |
| | 6 | The same amount is added or subtracted to make them equal. |
| **45** | 7 | **a.** 120p    **b.** 175p |
| | 8 | **a.** £1.45    **b.** £2.90 |
| | 9 | **a.** Example of bar model is shown below, Fahmida had £20    **b.** £32 <br><br> \| £5 \| £5 \| £5 \| £5 \| <br> \| £20 \| |
| | 10 | **a.** Example of bar model is shown below, Hamish had £30.    **b.** £60 <br><br> \| £10 \| £10 \| £10 \| <br> \| £30 \| |
| **47** | 1 | **a.** 240 minutes    **b.** 480 minutes |
| | 2 | **a.** 28 days    **b.** 56 days |
| | 3 | **a.** 20 minutes past eight or 8:20 <br> **b.** 25 minutes to four, 35 minutes past three or 3:35 <br> **c.** Ten minutes to two, fifty minutes past one or 1:50 |
| **48** | 4 | **a.** Half past 11 or 11:30 <br> **b.** 12 o'clock or 12:00 <br> **c.** quarter to one, 45 minutes past 12 or 12:45 <br> **d.** quarter past one, 15 minutes past one or 1:15 |
| | 5 | **a.** 45 minutes **b.** 1 hour 15 minutes **c.** 50 minutes **d.** 1 hour 5 minutes |
| **50** | 1 | |
| | 2 | 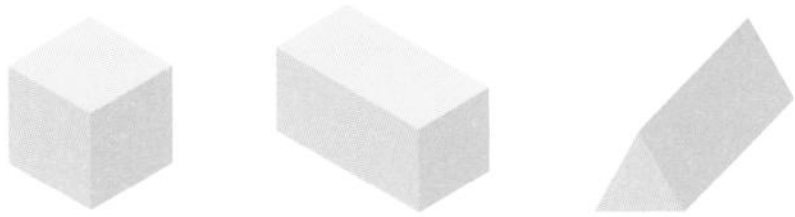 |
| | 3 | square-based pyramid |
| | 4 | cube |
| | 5 | cone |
| **52** | 1 | Accept any three triangles. |
| | 2 | Accept any quadrilaterals. |
| | 3 | 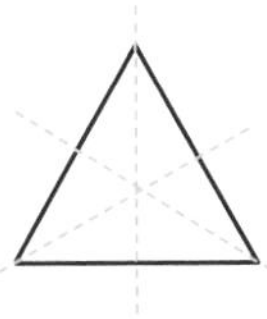 <br> 3 lines of symmetry |
| | 4 | 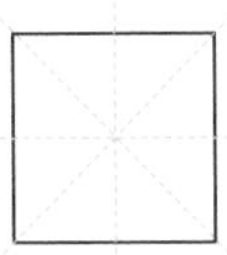 <br> 4 lines of symmetry |

# ANSWERS

| Page | Q | Answers |
|------|---|---------|
| 54 | 1 | The circle is in **between** the triangles. |
| | 2 | The triangles are **underneath** the circle. |
| | 3 | 4 |
| | 4 | ✓  ✓ |
| | 5 | A quarter turn |
| 55 | 6 | Accept answers that suggest the turn is in the same direction that the hands move on a clock. |
| | 7 | Accept answers that suggest the turn is in the opposite direction that the hands move on a clock. |
| | 8 | Accept answers such as: Forward four squares. Turn left or take a quarter turn anticlockwise. Forward two squares. Turn left or take a quarter turn anticlockwise. Forward three squares. Turn right or take a quarter turn clockwise. Forward two squares. Turn right or take a quarter turn clockwise. Forward four squares. |

**58 — 1**

a.

| Favourite pet | Tally | Number of children |
|---------------|-------|--------------------|
| Dog | ЖЖ ЖЖ II | 12 |
| Cat | ЖЖ IIII | 9 |
| Rabbit | ЖЖ II | 7 |
| Hamster | ЖЖ I | 6 |
| Guinea pig | ЖЖ III | 8 |

b. Accept any information that is correct.

c.

| Favourite pet | Number of children |
|---------------|--------------------|
| Dog | ● ● ● ● ● ● |
| Cat | ● ● ● ● ◖ |
| Rabbit | ● ● ● ◖ |
| Hamster | ● ● ● |
| Guinea pig | ● ● ● ● |

d. 42

**59 — 2**

a. 12    b. 2    c. 24

d. Accept any three questions whose answers can be interpreted from the block diagram.